CHILDSPLAY

The Medau Method is fully supported by the
Sports Establishment. The Medau Society is grant-aided
by the Sports Council and is a member of the
Central Council of Physical Recreation

CHILDSPLAY

Movement games for fun and fitness

LUCY JACKSON

Featuring Lala Manners

and Harriet (Pobs) Manners

Thorsons

An Imprint of HarperCollins*Publishers*

Thorsons
An imprint of HarperCollins*Publishers*
77–85 Fulham Palace Road
London W6 8JB

Published by Thorsons 1993

10 9 8 7 6 5 4 3 2 1

(c) Lucy Jackson 1993

Lucy Jackson asserts the moral right to
be identified as the author of this work

A catalogue record for this book
is available from the British Library

ISBN 0 7225 2780 2

Printed in Great Britain by
Butler & Tanner Ltd., Frome, Somerset

For my Mother
With loving thanks for her kindness

CONTENTS

ACKNOWLEDGEMENTS

〜〜〜

My special thanks to my daughter Lala Manners whose expertise has contributed so much to the writing of this book.

To my granddaughter Harriet Manners (Pobs) for her joyful part in the pictures.

To my son James Heitz Jackson for his help and advice with the manuscript.

To all the children who, over many years, have never ceased to surprise and enchant me.

I acknowledge with thanks the professional advice of my husband, Ian Jackson, FRCS, FRCOG; my nephew Andrew Jackson, FRCS; Barbara Dale; Chris Laubin, BA Hons, Int Montessori Dip; and Lesley Johnson BSC Hons, RCST.

Hair and make-up by Anne Buchanan, and thanks and appreciation to Catherine Ashmore for her miraculous pictures.

CHILDSPLAY – WHAT IS IT?

ChildsPlay takes the long view that childhood is a preparation for life.

It is not about producing the perfect child who conforms to every known achievement grid. It is about allowing time to enjoy and understand the rapid changes of development in the first five years.

Beginning with the aim of fit, strong bodies, ChildsPlay works on many levels.

◆ It preserves the child's natural energy and love of life, and helps to restore your own.

◆ It promotes safety and confidence and mutual respect.

◆ It is about acquiring social skills and the basic tools of learning in a way which is as natural as breathing.

◆ It is about loving and caring and understanding.

ChildsPlay is a must for you — and every child.

INTRODUCTION

~~~

TIME, SPACE AND A KINDLY ADULT

I loved being a child. There were few experts on childhood around in the 1920s and 30s peddling advice, no talent spotters within the family looking for 'potential'. No-one fussed about us. There was no hectic programme to stimulate our minds and shape our personalities.

The daily routine was fixed and recognizable, changing only with the seasons. Organized activities were few. The glimpse of a fire engine or buying summer sandals provided pinnacles of excitement.

Compared with today, toys and books were minimal. Radio programmes for children were unknown, and television uninvented. The gift of a wind-up gramophone brought hours of unimagined delight.

With an adored older brother and enough small friends, we were never bored. Though never taught anything directly, I cannot remember being unable to read, write, count and sing.

My memory is that we played and played like puppies. We understood, however, what was considered 'acceptable' behaviour, and though frequently at odds with the grown-ups through our wilder deeds of derring-do, our promises to behave were heartfelt and extravagant.

Complaints that we were 'too noisy and too restless' left us chastened and repentant. But we never doubted the intuitive generosity and complete acceptance of ourselves by the adult world around us.

We were independent, bright, resourceful and irrepressible; nothing ever seemed 'too bad'. All seemed contained in a cocoon of kindness in which we grew in our own time and manner.

No-one could or should put the clock back. The world moves on and childhood reflects and is part of life, as it is now. The pace, the priorities and the possibilities alter with each generation.

But the essential child never changes. Tears and laughing feel the same. The need for love and justice are still the unseen passions. That small person who is and was ourselves is the world's universal citizen, ageless and unaltered.

My cosy pre-war nursery world has gone, but have we also lost the vital ingredients that make childhood a safe springboard for life? Bombarded with advice, plagued by advertising, exhorted to 'fulfil' ourselves in every possible way, taught to distrust our instincts, have we lost the gentle art of nurturing our young?

Is the pace too great? Are our children being pressurized and over programmed? Has the desperate scramble to compete and conform brought the rat race into the nursery? We cannot change the world. The pressures are real. Sadness and pain are part, inevitably, of everyone's experience. Ambition and the desire to succeed and 'stretch' ourselves are legitimate goals. But we need to begin gently.

Childhood is not an end in itself, but an ongoing preparation for the next big step — a continuous rite of passage. We cannot overestimate the effect on all of us of those intensely vivid first five years. It is an indisputable fact that they colour our attitudes for a lifetime.

Through years of watching, teaching and loving small children, I am saddened that ever fewer adults look back to their childhood years for laughter, solace and strength.

With the more gentle 'feel' of the 90s, is it time for a more intuitive approach? Time to redress the balance? ChildsPlay is a plea, a cry from the heart if you like, that happiness does matter. It is not a plaintive dream of 'back to the Ark'. It is not a forlorn hope, but a positive change of attitude and practice. It is a way through the speed and scramble of modern living to take the pressure off children and to re-assess their primary needs.

There are no costly toys and elaborate apparatus, no designer gear and action-packed schedules. It is much simpler than that. After the bare necessities and a few small friends, children need:

TIME –
to do things at their own pace,
SPACE –
to experiment and make mistakes, and
A KINDLY ADULT –
to supervise gently and help when needed.

ChildsPlay is about success and achievement, about surviving and coping. It is about understanding and doing the best for ourselves. But it is also about recognizing happiness and preserving the instinctive energy and joy in living which is characteristic of the young of all species. These formative years can never be relived. The patterns of change are rapid and highly charged.

ChildsPlay assures that everyone can say: "I loved being a child".

THE CHANGING STYLES OF CHILDHOOD

My Children of the 60s

My daughter Lala and twin sons, Julian and James, had less than three years between them. From the start they were a 'Gang of Three' and a force to be reckoned with. There were many times when the pandemonium seemed beyond good sense and they surely needed a firmer hand. Easier said than done.

Even with help, space to play, a garden and long experience as a teacher, the 24-hours-a-day shift came as a shock. Rain or shine, in sickness and in health, seemingly oblivious to one's own needs or state of exhaustion, children never give up for a moment. This is the instinct to survive at its most primitive and demanding.

The extraordinary and relentless pressure of living with lively children left me often tearful and exasperated. I think it helps to realize that it is often sheer exhaustion that can make coping with children at times such a disaster area. Though significant and memorable for me, those were the bad moments.

We did have a lot of fun, and like many women of my generation I adored the daily round of walks and play, the seemingly magical growth patterns, the learning of each new skill, the fresh minds, the instant affection.

The time was the opulent 'Swinging Sixties'. Colours were bright, the Beatles sang of Love, Love, Love, and everybody danced. Children were the 'in thing', Dr Spock's book on easy-going childcare was the only reference.

My three were inevitably children of the 60s and there were sharp contrasts with my childhood in the 30s. They were undoubtedly less directly disciplined, less contrite over mishaps and probably more indulged. Clothes were more comfortable and easy-care. Nursery food was tastier, the house was warmer and there were sunny holidays abroad. Television was rationed, but there were mountains of toys and an endless supply of books, paints, puzzles and Playdo.

Despite the differences, talking to them now, it seems that their memories of childhood are not too different from mine. Time seemed endless, space was more than enough. Someone was always there for them. The three essentials had remained intact, the link with the past unbroken. They were kind and charming children, great enthusiasts and full of ideas. As adults now, I would choose them for my friends.

The 70s and 80s

Each new decade brings criticism of the one before. Was anyone really serious about all the 60s 'Peace, man' and 'Getting with it'? Did anyone actually follow Dr Spock to the letter? Even taking account of this inevitable rejection of a previous time, I do feel that through the 70s and 80s life has become much more difficult for the under-fives.

No longer the pampered darlings of the 60s, it is sometimes difficult to see just what role children do play in all our lives. Expensive accessories whose appearance is planned with split-second accuracy? Some sort of future investment whose every potential talent must be cultivated by experts alone? 'Love' objects who must nevertheless not interrupt or

interfere with our 'real' lives of work and personal fulfilment?

Even within vast individual differences, being a child is far less comfortable. Today, time is a vanishing commodity. Children's schedules have become as crowded as their parents'. Space is increasingly restricted and no longer safe for children. Gone are the street games and groups of children playing alone in the parks.

Though fathers, in theory anyway, take on more practical responsibilities than ever before, kindly adults are always at a premium. Families are smaller and often widely dispersed. Childcare is frequently inexpert and tends to come and go. Children are missing out on the three great essential needs.

ChildsPlay will show you how, in the easiest most natural way, to restore the balance. You will discover a new freedom and pleasure in each other's company, making the best of your time together. You will see an improved fitness, increased confidence and general ability to cope.

You will all be happier and healthier, which in the end, in a list of high priorities, is what matters most.

1 THE ROOTS OF THE CHILDSPLAY APPROACH

To understand the concepts and teaching behind ChildsPlay, we need to study the work of Heinrich Medau. He was the son of a farmer in northern Germany. He always remembered how, with a gang of young friends, he used to roam the countryside.

They learned to run, climb, leap and swim with all the enthusiasm of young boys. He called it 'natural gymnastics' – they were very proficient though quite untaught. He was a gifted musician and subsequently trained as a teacher in music and gymnastics.

He was very impressed by the influential educationalists of the time, Steiner, Froebel and Maria Montessori, who had all reacted against the strict schoolroom discipline of the 19th century. Recalling the freedom of his own youth, it distressed him that the jerky, rigorous, military-based exercise he had to teach his small pupils seemed to cut across their naturally supple, easy way of moving.

Medau always questioned the effectiveness of repetitive machine-like exercise. He saw its potential danger to the young body, its contradictions of everything a young child needed or wanted to do. When in the 1920s new ideas about 'natural movement' were being discussed, it struck an immediate chord of recognition. Hinrich and his wife Senta established their own teacher training college in Berlin in 1929. They were very much in the mainstream of PE for women and soon became famous as teachers of the new style – 'organic whole body movement' – which was gradually replacing the jerky, stilted, free-standing exercises.

The work was highly innovative and creative and provided an entirely different approach to teaching PE. Medau said always that in order to understand how the body should move he studied the movements of small children. He discovered that they moved 'in one piece' like a body-stocking, never isolating groups of muscles. The co-ordination and correct body-alignment seemed instinctive and they always knew exactly how to alternate rest with

effort, never in any way over-stressing themselves.

As a brilliant pianist he loved their boundless energy, and joyful response to music and rhythm. Most characteristic of all was that their movement expressed 'everything' about them – their age and stage of development, their personalities and general health. This was the post-Isadora Duncan era, and with other teachers of the time he recognized the immense significance of movement to the young child's mental and emotional development. Montessori's statement that movement cannot be divorced from life, and that it is a source of energy and delight, could have been made by Medau himself.

He noted, again with all the educationalists of his era, the child's delight in toys and any 'hand apparatus' he found in the school. He used clubs, balls and hoops in new and exciting ways to teach co-ordination and new skills. He waited for the children to discover and produce play patterns for themselves. Nothing was ever forced or imposed. The pace, the degree of effort, the fun, the motivation — everything had to be absolutely right for the child.

He was deeply concerned to preserve the energy and flowing ease of a child's movement into adulthood. And it is upon these principles of using movement patterns that are natural and right for the child that ChildsPlay is based. It is part of the joy and magic which you will discover with your child through moving together.

When I studied at the Medau school in the early 50s, some of the classes I most vividly recall were given by one of our teachers with a group of local children. They remain a blueprint for the children's work of today. The pacing, delicate adjustments made to suit each child, the organic development of the themes, was brilliant. The sense of fun and ease reflected the joy and confidence of everyone. Nothing was taught directly within this context, all were free to experiment. Every version of a

step or movement was approved. Their physical skill, delighted response to music and rhythm, the easy respect for each other and their teacher, the harmony within the group, meant that 'everything' was there. Even now, forty years on, it is probably the best work with children I have ever seen done anywhere in the world.

Medau's free-flowing, easily adaptable improvized teaching method based on observation of the special needs of the individual or group is most natural to the child's own approach. It is upon this universally successful and time-honoured method that ChildsPlay is based. It accounts also for the huge popularity and success of our work with children which prompted originally the writing of this book.

The Rhythm of Life

One of the world's great mysteries is the human response to rhythm. What is it anyway? A great vibrant energy, the 'life force itself', or is it about marching in step or head banging in a rock concert? Even more difficult is what it means when artists talk of rhythm in a painting or the facade of a building. Rhythm in speech, rhythm in poetry, rhythm of the seasons, rhythm of the tides, day and night, sleep and waking – and this is before the rhythm of bird song, music and dance is mentioned.

What about the bio- or body-rhythms – the ebb and flow of energy, the digestion, the menstrual cycle, the breathing rhythm and the heart beat. Perhaps we can think of rhythm as perceived patterns in time and space. There has to be some sort of recognizable repetition, balance and flow. By what magic does our body work in harmony...by what strange mystery do biophysicists tell us that the 'diseased cell produces a freak rhythm'?

Perhaps rhythm is the force that organizes chaos, and allows us to use a form of shorthand, an economy of effort, to balance our bodies and minds, keeping us in touch with ourselves and our stake in the universe.

Nothing that we say about the power and effect of rhythm on our lives can be too exaggerated. With new knowledge about changes in body chemistry brought about by rhythmic movement, it is becoming even more significant.

Perhaps it all begins in the womb with the experience of our mother's body rhythms. No-one really knows but you will find, as Medau did, that your child will respond to rhythm with a curious rapture. Everything you do during your class time, every game you play together, needs to be done rhythmically.

It helps with the smallest tasks. I've never been a good packer of suitcases. Preparing three excited children and a maze of odd socks and lost swimsuits for the holidays used to drive me to distraction. Even as a very small boy, James used to save the day by suggesting we should play 'some loud marching music' which showed great insight and suited my predicament to perfection. I imagined anyway that I grew calmer and more efficient!

'SHALL WE DANCE?'

My daughter, Lala, whose name is Lanya Mary, and her daughter, Pobs, whose name is Harriet, have both done ChildsPlay since they were born. It is second nature, and a way of 'being' rather than something separate and belonging only to 'class time'. Lala is in any case extremely well known for her work with children. Pobs was three when these pictures were taken. As with all small children, she is no angel, but full of ideas and determined to make them work. Lala's adult role seems more passive.

But their fitness, infectious joy and mutual delight in movement and in one another, is obvious. This is not showbiz or any sort of performance. It is a small child, any small child, having fun, keeping fit and acquiring skills and knowledge in the most natural way.

Because Pobs is a girl, 'the child' is referred to as 'her' throughout the book. This was a purely practical decision, and everything has an equal and identical application to the needs of boys, In truth, anyone and everyone can do it.

You and your child will love it. This is ChildsPlay in its very essence.

2 PREGNANCY, BIRTH AND THE FIRST FEW WEEKS

Let's begin at the beginning. This chapter is written for mothers, but any pregnancy affects us all, not least fathers and partners.

When you are pregnant, even more than at any other time, you need to do what feels right for you. You are not an invalid, but there are enormous changes taking place involving both mind and body, which take some getting used to. Follow the miraculous patterns of change with an increased awareness that often comes with pregnancy. There are thousands of years of experience behind what your body is doing, and you can safely trust in its wisdom. You may feel a bit tired and sick during the first three months. Once the placenta becomes more secure, progesterone levels rise, and this phase usually passes and you are over the first milestone.

Some women say that between the third and sixth months they never feel better or look prettier in their entire lives. If you are already into a fitness programme, keep it up with sensible adaptations. The relaxin in your body will make you more supple, in preparation for the birth. Be careful not to overextend the range of movement in your joints and make them unstable. Frequent and gentle exercise is best. Try the video and book package *Medau – The art of energy*. The video programme adapts easily to pregnancy and the book has some valuable advice on back problems and general body management.

Take Special Care Of Your Feet

They will be coping with your increased weight and deserve some extra attention. Comfortable feet in comfortable shoes are a must. They are the first essential for a feeling of ease, safety and well-being. Good posture begins with your feet. It is vital for your body to be correctly aligned to avoid overtaxing your back.

Make caring for your feet an on-going everyday affair. Whenever you remember, point and stretch your toes, then turn them up, pushing down your heels. Work them rhythmically like a pump which will help your circulation and lymphatic drainage. Take off your shoes and put your feet up higher than your pelvis whenever you can. Spread your toes and rotate your ankles — it always makes me yawn, relax and feel good.

Try to be Sensible About Your Diet

You are not by any means 'eating for two', but it does make for a conflict of interests if you cling to your slimmer figure. A good rule for pregnancy could be: health comes first, fitness second, and shape will have to wait.

There are some excellent specialist books on 'having babies'. Follow your own ante-natal programme conscientiously and try to understand the actual theory and process of birth. Don't imagine that the books by the experts will tell you everything. The best preparations and all the jargon seldom match up on the day. You can sometimes feel you've come on the wrong night to the wrong show.

More that anything, you need the peace and quiet to follow your own body instincts. Feel confident and free to choose whether you want to be alone or need your partner or someone to counsel you through it. The choice should be yours. Be aware that the professional responsibility lies with the doctors and/or midwife. You need to understand and respect each other's opinions from the start. Whether you feel drawn to high tech or natural childbirth, leave your options open. Don't get hung up on what some experts call 'essential birthing'.

The Birth

Giving birth is a unique and intensly private experience. Deeply felt and emotionally charged, it can leave indelible impressions. Each time is different; go along with it and be glad whichever way it happens. Remember too that a caesarian section is safer than a difficult delivery. Sometimes the build-up and new 'awareness' of birth can make it something of an end in itself. It is, after all, only the beginning. A healthy, unstressed baby takes priority over the picture book and considered more video-worthy 'natural' birth. Whichever way you manage, it is a miracle and you have every reason to be proud and thrilled.

Some people think that the birth is the easy bit. In those first weeks it is the small baby's never-ending demands that come as a shock. You will probably never ever feel so exhausted again. Discomfort and soreness after the birth, feeding problems, lack of sleep or a crying baby alone can provoke gales of despair. Tears can seem frequent and unstoppable. Cry when you like – we've all done it and it will pass. Looking back, it seems a small trauma. A few turns as a drama queen are unlikely to develop into classic baby blues.

Seek and accept all the help you can get. Whether it is help with the ironing, a good night's sleep or time with the other children, line up everyone you can think of to help you. These are precious weeks and pass in a flash. It is a pity to lose them in a fog of dismay. Pamper yourself a little and take time off to counter the depressing 'I feel an awful mess'. Clean hair, fresh clothes, clean knicks and a good maternity bra all help.

The First Weeks

Long luxury baths are also a great comfort. When you feel ready, do some wriggling and stretching as you soak. Pull up your knees one at a time, then stretch out your legs over the taps, easing out your lower back. Support yourself with your arms and put both feet up on one side of the bath. Pull in your tummy and hold for a count of 8. Keeping your knees bent, put your feet down and slide your legs out in front. Wiggle your toes, then lift your feet up on the other side.

Make up some variations. Support yourself with your hands and twist your hips gently. The warm water will lift you. You can enjoy being able to see your feet, and pull up your knees over your 'new' flat tummy again!

You can progress to some of your post-natal exercises as soon as they seem comfortable. Your pelvic floor 'pull-ins' are a good idea. You need to begin somewhere and the bath is the best place. Try singing in the bath. It need not be too operatic or demanding. Humming or making chanting sounds on a long slow out-breath is a start. It stimulates your breathing and the vibrations in your head and chest are very therapeutic and cheering.

Four Weeks Plus

By four weeks with luck, no setbacks and a baby who sleeps well, you will have rejoined the human race. Time now to think of some positive post-natal programme. Forget the relaxation bit – you will probably feel pretty floppy anyway. One real consideration is that pregnancy tends to exaggerate any small weakness you may have. An old injury, a wobbly knee or ankle, back-ache or weak arches in your feet, anaemia, insomnia, sore gums will almost certainly have reappeared. The list is endless.

Now is the time to nurse your body and be very positive about 'repairing' the weaknesses. You will need to look for energy and strength. Exhaustion spoils everything.

Here is a 15-minute daily pro-gramme to start you off:

Find a time when your energy is not too low and refuse to be dis-turbed. Have a quick tidy round and lie on your back on top of your bed, head on a pillow and another pillow under slightly bent knees. Play some music you like or listen to the radio. You need to be stimulated — 'looking for energy' — not bored.

Set your own pace, allow yourself to pause, and yawn when you like. Run your fingers and thumbs through your hair. Massage the scalp with the fingertips, squeezing and gripping. Run your hands down to the back of the neck (like a mother cat) and squeeze strongly. Cup your ears with your hands — warm them, squeezing gently and releasing. Listen to the sound as you breathe out slowly.

Soothe and Stimulate Your Face

Cup your eyes — close them and open them as you run your hands up into your hair line. Holding one hand across the forehead, lightly pat your face with your fingertips. Go round in a circle, reverse the directions. Change hands. At any time you wish, stretch out or change the position of your legs. Yawn when you like. Pat your mouth firmly with one hand going across sideways from ear to ear. Change the shape of your lips, saying 'a-e-i-o-u' or make Red Indian noises.

Massage the side of your neck and down to the shoulders with opposite hands, one at a time. Ease out your neck, turning your head gently. Yawn and gasp when you like. Breathe deeply.

Warming Up The Joints

Cross your hands over to cup your shoulders — rub and massage them vigorously. Squeeze your upper arms with your hands, moving down to your elbows. Cup and warm them as you did your shoulders. Rub your hands together, then the back of each hand. Flick your fingers out from the palm. Rub your knees, feet and back of the ankles.

Be kind but firm with yourself — don't persuade anyone to do it for you, unless you are going to sleep. *You are looking for energy and stimulation when you do it yourself, not relaxation.*

Strengthening And Tightening Your Muscles

Involve your whole body – not just parts of it. Curl up on your side around a pillow in the foetal position. Squeeze hard and pull in your tummy strongly. Stretch out on your back and curl up on the other side – hold for a slow count of 12 in each position. Concentrate and tighten every muscle you can find – thighs, buttocks, arms, back. Hold on for dear life and then stretch out again – exquisite relief – on to your back. Feel the effort and enjoy the change from tension to release. Breathe freely. Repeat until you feel you've had plenty.

Tightening Your Thighs And Pelvic Floor

Return to your original position on your back, with knees bent. Grip a pillow between your knees, tightening the inner thighs, buttocks and pulling up the pelvic floor. Repeat 8 times fairly fast. Now do the same move-ment, but tug the pillow with both hands, pulling in your tummy strongly. Change the pace and the intensity.

As you grow stronger, you will be able to get your head and shoulders off the pillow. Stretch out and yawn. Turn your head gently and tuck in your chin. You should feel great and getting stronger every day.

When your baby is eight weeks old, and always provided there have been no specific problems, you can and should be doing your post-natal exercises very conscientiously.

Always avoid standing when you can sit, and lie down to rest your back whenever it is feasible. Don't rush back to playing tennis or doing your fitness classes until after the tenth week. Have plenty of fresh air and gentle walks, and be as fussy and fastidious as you like.

Remember, at this stage, that health comes first, fitness a poor second, and your shape will have to wait.

3 BABY MOVES –
THE FIRST YEAR

Babies have done rather well over the last ten years. There are many excellent books full of sensible advice. Gone are the rigid regimes and fixed feeding times. Try to be as flexible as possible in the first few weeks – easier with a first baby – adapting the days and nights to her patterns of sleeping and feeding. Babies set their own pace and you need to 'cosy-down' together. Do 'anything' to stop the crying – it is meant to provoke you. Whether you are breast- or bottle-feeding, take sensible advice about feeding and ask for help if you are battling. Some mothers find this 'formless' day incredibly difficult, and long for some sort of routine.

Planning your day
Set your own schedule if you feel better, but remember that you need rest more than a chic hairdo at this stage. Do your routine in the bath (page 22) and your energy programme.

Babies are born with all their body systems intact. We know now that they react to outside stimuli such as sound and light even in the womb. The orchestra of body 'sounds' – the 'swishing' heartbeat, the breathing pressure changing, the digestive waves – must all have been felt. With time and space to move and rest, plus a kindly adult to supervise, you could say that ChildsPlay begins in the womb.

Babies from the start like firm, warm hands, not cold feather fingers. We all have a healing power in our hands and babies need to be held in a strong but gentle grip. They are not made of Dresden china and are happiest being bathed, winded, cradled and carried far more 'robustly' than some people imagine suitable for such tiny bodies.

Some babies may have to recover from birth trauma or an uneasy digestion and take time to settle in. Most of them love to be rocked, patted and jiggled from day one – a rocking chair is a joy, good for baby and mother. It is, after all, an extension of life in the womb, rocking and swaying gently.

How to begin

Calm babies will enjoy doing their ChildsPlay on your lap almost at once. Sit comfortably. Put her on her back facing you. Play some music if it makes you feel cheerful and motivated. Moving very slowly, with a firm but gentle touch, hold her arms with your thumbs in the palms of her hands. In the first few days, she will grip quite strongly. Open her arms out sideways, then cross them over her chest. Move them gently up and down like signalling flags – then out in any direction.

Lean forward (pulling in your tummy!) and talk or sing to her. Pretend to pull her up. Slip a hand under her head and rock her gently forwards and backwards, easing out your lower back. Hold her legs under the knees and press them gently towards her chest, rounding her back. Press gently sideways and outwards – 'Frog's Legs'. Lift her feet upwards, gently raising her bottom. Pull in your tummy and sit up straight with each lift.

Massage and stimulate her feet, thumbs on the soles and squeezing gently. Rub her tummy and chest, fingers up under her chin. Turn her sideways and rub her back and bottom in small circular movements. Feel the tiny vertebrae up and down her spine.

Talk and sing to her, make clicking noises. Cup her ears with your hands and gently turn her head sideways. Watch her little body follow round in perfect alignment. Always move slowly and 'tell' her what you are doing. Babies are like little jugs full of milk, and tend to spill over rather easily.

'Improvize' the play, and do what seems fun. Follow every instinct to play, being and sounding as daft as you like.

Put her on a towel and waterproof sheet beside you when you're doing your post-natal exercises. Take those wretched nappies off so that she can kick and move freely. Roll her over on to her tummy – put her toys around for her to grasp or focus on. Hold her up under her arms to 'bounce' on her feet, while supporting her weight. The strength of those knee thrusts is extraordinary.

In a very short time, she will recognize her 'play' time with you. Try to include her in your post-natal exercises. Pobs used to crawl along Lala's legs when she was reaching backwards and 'doing her abdominals'.

Fun moves

Babies love what we call 'movement experience' – high lifts and drops, being swished about and turned upside-down – but not after a feed. Make it a real 'Love-In' with lots of kisses, hugs and laughing. Sing to her and play all the old baby games. (See page 91 – 92.) You are far better rolling about, stretching and improvising an exercise programme at this stage, than gritting your teeth and forcing yourself to repeat sets of exercises that bore you to tears.

Pobs was five months old when the picture below was taken. She knew all about 'her class' by this time. She loved the squidgy ball and was very adept at gripping it between hands and feet and pressing her mouth against it. She used to shriek and laugh, rolling over to follow it when it rolled away.

By seven or eight months, rocking on hands and knees often becomes a favourite, con-suming occupation. It is a preparation for crawling and strengthens legs and back too. Rock with her, stretching your back as you sit on your heels, pulling in your tummy as you go forward. Once she can roll over, make sure you exercise on the floor. Sliding off a bed is a too frequent adventure.

Small backs are safest sleeping flat. Try to avoid leaving her for hours slumped in a buggy or push-chair.

The first months will slip past with incredible speed. Smiling, laughing, sitting up and crawling all happen, along with increased weight and strength in very predictable patterns. Your own strength and energy will steadily improve, and exercising and playing together will heighten your awareness and enjoyment of her development.

This is a good time to look at these amazing patterns of development. It will give you a clearer understanding of how children cope with the changes.

4 PATTERNS OF DEVELOPMENT

Change and development are what childhood is about. In five brief, hectic years the tiny, helpless baby becomes a recognizable person, physically competent, socially aware and with all her basic educational skills in place.

The vitality and speed of change is astonishing. Growing up is like a complex, fast-moving game, where not only the rules and goal posts keep changing, but also the players themselves. Keeping a cool head, and understanding the natural and inevitable changes can be a daunting task for you and your child.

Investigating childhood development has been a growth industry. There are many excellent books to tell you when to expect the first smile, first sit-up or first step. All this advice can be reassuring as it gives fair warning of changes ahead. Don't however be anxious or blinded by science. Children vary enormously and, in any case, early development has little to do with ultimate achievement.

There has been a fashion to exploit the learning potential of these early years: 'Stimulate them – children absorb things so easily', the pundits say. Why not learn to skate, ski, speak French and play the fiddle quite apart from play group, school, hectic socializing 'they have more invitations than we do' and non-stop television. Why not indeed?

Simply because there is so much happening already.

Children need time to get to grips with themselves. They need time to savour the changes and keep in touch at every level. They need time to build up inner resources of strength and understanding.

When children develop, it seems that the whole person goes through quite definite phases. Psychologists would have us believe in deep, unconscious conflicts and elaborate attachments. Who knows? I only know that puppies, kittens and even small birds in my care go through similar very recognizable patterns with the requisite changes of personality. Presumably this has nothing to do with psychology and more to do with nerve pathways and physical development.

These changes seem to arise quite spontaneously. It is important to have enough time to focus on a new interest or skill exactly when it happens. This corresponds to what Maria Montessori called 'sensitive periods', when the child is especially open to a certain interest. She felt that once missed, the opportunity was gone forever and that the natural flow of development had been in some way blocked.

Childhood is more a happening than a production. Temperaments vary vastly and sometimes we ourselves are more in tune with different stages. Some of us enjoy the riotous 'twos' and 'fours' more than the more co-operative 'threes' and 'fives'. Everything is relative anyway. What may be considered high temperament in one setting seems like placid calm in another.

In every case, it is your child's understanding of herself that is the first task of childhood. Character and temperament need to settle and be explored. Personality needs time to integrate. Strengths,

weaknesses, likes, dislikes and making choices, need to be understood. This is an intuitive inner process, not a jargon journey, and every child needs time and space to do it for herself. It is an adventure which requires no overload of endless entertainment or programme of study.

A deep sense of self-awareness is the beginning of confidence and achievement.

It is too easy for a child to reach the age of five, breathless and confused, tutored in every conceivable skill, all set to keep up, but asking forlornly, 'Who am I?'

Time to practise, space for making mistakes, and kindly supervision is the best 'Do-It-Yourself' basis for the under-fives. There are years of high-pressure learning ahead. At this stage the experience of direct teaching should be only a gentle extra.

CONVERSATIONS WITH AN ARMCHAIR

It is amusing to plot the changes in both physical skill and areas of interest and 'public' persona through 'conversations with an armchair':

Under One Year
Faced with a chair, the baby would crawl towards it, hands out and

mouth open to feel and taste the texture of the fabric. Any studs or patterns would be minutely examined. 'Things' would be pushed to disappear underneath. She might roll over to examine it at a different angle. You could laugh and play 'peek-a-boo' over and around. Everyone who will make her smile and show her new things to 'investigate' is her friend.

One Year

At about a year, and sometimes earlier, she will begin to pull up into standing. The bopping and knee bouncing is continuous, strengthening the postural muscles. There are smiles of delight and chatty noises. Hands would be patted up and down, first together and then singly, then suddenly released, followed by a dramatic 'sit down'. Attempts to stagger round the chair holding on or even balancing are the natural progression

towards walking. All is charm and sweetness. Special affection will be shown to her 'favourites'.

Two Years

By two years the change is dramatic, and 'battling Billy/Betty' has appeared. The large muscle groups in legs, back and buttocks are developing, walking and running have been mastered and

the climbing begins. Heaving themselves up, bouncing and stamping, bailing out the cushions, refusing to be helped, refusing to get down and

in energy and restlessness can be exhausting. Strength seems ahead of skill and they exasperate themselves as much as their minders.

Three Years

By three they are often more friendly and co-operative, anxious to share and talk. 'Mothering' is sometimes an obsession, with endless games of teddies and dollies being put to bed, walked outside and cared for. They are quite likely to sit, wanting you to join them on the chair. Hand-eye co-ordination is good, stickers and threading beads, books and stories are favourites.

They understand cause and effect

refusing to share the seat is fairly routine. The 'twos' tend to be reckless, misjudging height and distance. They are still very top heavy and tip over easily. Crashes, tantrums, pushing, grabbing and shouting ''Mine'' are the general flavour. The increase

and spot hazards quickly – 'I'm climbing up to balance here and will you be ready to catch me please.' Their physical skills are more focussed and careful. The chair could be a boat, bed for teddy, house or car. They sing and mimic, and there are short bursts of highly imaginative play. There are bouts of totally unrealistic hide and seek – usually 'hiding' their faces and keeping very still. It always seems to me a deeply primitive survival 'protection' instinct. They love to laugh and joke and will sit on the chair asking 'Why?...Why?', often providing the answers for themselves and you. I have tried to avoid making vast distinctions between boys and girls, but it is very important to allow boys to experience this phase of strong identification with more traditional female roles.

Four Years

By four there is an enormous increase in physical strength. The back straightens up and the knees and hips are more stable. The buttocks are strong, the child is kicking, running, climbing, jumping, competing: 'I'm first' is the cry. They turn from hiders into hunters with 'surprise attacks', launching themselves on to your back, the chair or other children.

'I'm faster'...'I can catch you'. The noise can be alarming. The arm chair will be pushed, leaped upon, rocked and tipped over. You will rarely be invited to join in except to carry out instructions. They tend to lose their baby plumpness and are, for some, less physically appealing. They need some real discipline to avoid accidents and unacceptable assertiveness. Don't worry about sibling rivalry, the new school, or the wrong birth sign making him or her aggressive and unmanageable. Testing your muscles and your parents' patience is what being four is often about.

Daddy, or men generally, tend to be in favour, with an element of hero-worship and admiration. 'My dad's the biggest, the strongest, the best driver' – are routine comments.

Five Years

By five they can be quite accomplished performers. Proper tricks will be practised and improved upon. They can be quite self-critical and you may be asked to coach a head-over-heels on the chair or an attempted handstand. They often seem less physically wild than they were at four and can read, sing, tell stories and sustain long periods of fantasy play. The chair could be part of an elaborate house, school room or garage. It could also less rewardingly become a perch for hours of television viewing. There is usually less hero-worship and a great increase in interest in 'my best friends' and overall peer group.

Even a brief look at the changes achieved so quickly and inevitably does help to smooth the

way and keep a hold on what is happening. Go along with each new phase and try to give your child as much time and space as you can.

5 PATTERNS OF ENERGY

With slight variations of energy, small creatures when awake will move, play, wriggle and stretch constantly. Bursts of activity alternate with sudden complete 'flopping out' and even sleep. So it is with children. They seem to have a driving energy and almost obessional need to move which no amount of pleading to sit still and stop fidgeting can divert. They will then, quite as completely, come to rest, only to take off again and repeat the pattern. This behaviour, as we shall see, exactly suits their young body structure.

Health benefits

No specific work has been done on the effect of exercise on children's health. The chronically inactive child is a too-recent phenomenon. Studies on obese children in America, however, reveal some alarming physical and psychological problems.

Bodies are built to move. All adult studies show that body systems work more efficiently when regularly exercised. Improved circulation, digestion, lymphatic drainage, better muscle tone and the increased density of bone calcium are well documented. From circumstantial evidence alone, we can safely assume the same health benefits apply to children.

Children though are not mini-adults. Their bodies are growing and developing and differ significantly from adults:

◆ Their bones have a different calcium collagen content and are much softer, more flexible and relatively less strong than the ligaments attached to them. These strong ligaments protect the delicate joints. This is the opposite to the adult skeletal structure. The vital growing plates, epipheses and apopheses are soft and vulnerable. They, and the joints too, are easily damaged through overloading or too many repetitions of the same movement.

◆ Children's muscles are light and elastic. There is little bulk and therefore a complete inability to perform long, strong sustained movements. They need to move constantly and quickly, hence the endless bobbing and bouncing, wriggling and changing position. It accounts also for the sudden flopping and frequent need to rest. Tests show that children are wasteful of aerobic energy. The

haemoglobin in the blood which carries oxygen is different from adults and they tend to breathe rapidly and lightly.

◆ Their temperature control is not

efficient. They become quickly over-heated and tend not to sweat easily. 'I'm hot' or 'I'm thirsty' can mean real distress. On the other hand, they become chilled with equal speed, with no means of spontaneous recovery.

◆ Their nervous systems differ in the way nerve impulses are conducted. Hormone levels, unlike adults, show little difference between male and female. The most striking differ-ence is that as growth and the body's recovery systems are linked, children seem to 'get better' with aston-ishing speed. Down one

minute and up the next — fevers, falls, like tantrums and tears, are quickly forgotten.

But children can play only in the middle ground, in all aspects of their lives. There are very distinct limits, and a child has few reserves of strength to recov-er from any form of extreme trauma. If we consider the young body's need in an ideal world to move quickly, lightly and continuously, with frequent periods of self-deter-mined rest, we can see that it matches up exactly with the child's quite different time scale. Their con-centration span is far shorter with rapid and continuous changes of interest.

There is a driving need to do things his/her own way. Then there are the sudden, seemingly inexplicable bouts of exhaustion. Nothing can be more opposed to the steadier 'long-term result' and much more focussed adult world. It can prove something of a collision course.

One of the great benefits of ChildsPlay is to provide for your child a time and space to do things his/her way. Setting the pace within the right timescale, being able to choose or discard an activity, contributing ideas and never being 'wrong' is a valu-able relief to a pressured child.

THE FITNESS WORKOUT

6 THE FITNESS MESSAGE

Who needs a work-out anyway? It is perfectly true that small children, given enough time, space and a kindly adult, will 'play' themselves into being as fit as they ever can be.

Their energy and natural curiosity about themselves and the world around them compels them to non-stop testing and experiment. (See page 34.) In an idyllic state of nature rest, sleep and food would be taken as required, rather like little foxes in the wild. This is of course totally impractical for life as it is today. Children are part of society and have to fit in and match up with other people's lives. (See page 99.)

What do we mean by fitness anyway?

We mean being able to sustain a 'suitable' lifestyle with ease and pleasure, cope with crises and develop our best potential. Being physically fit is where we should all begin.

Sadly, there are woeful tales of far too many children being overweight, inactive and physically unskilled. It sometimes comes as a shock to monitor over a week how many hours a child spends 'tied down' in a car seat, buggy or high-chair, or watching the television. This wastes valuable play time. Fast food can seem almost addictive, and the compulsion to munch crisps and eat sweets can be very fattening. There is thus every need to find time to exercise together.

If begun in childhood, being responsible and in control, and feeling good about your body, can last a lifetime. *The fitness message needs to be built into mind and body in the first five years.* The habit of 'well being' should be part of everyone's basic kit for life.

The programme is based on what are called the 'fitness factors': Stretch, Strength, Mobility, Stamina (Fun Stunts) and Skills, specially adapted for you and your child.

That 'Special' Atmosphere

Remember that children are not masochists. They will never repeat anything that hurts or bores them. You need to start gently and let them set the pace. Use their ideas. You are equal 'partners' in the games. Children are so much on the receiving end and this is her big chance to contribute. You need to change tack quickly if she is becoming bored or unruly.

Be very encouraging and enjoy the way she learns new skills. It is not a competition, nothing is 'wrong', and try to be positive. 'How clever you are', and 'Let's try this way', are more quickly understood than 'Don't do that'.

Never be cross during your class time. You will need to be flexible and remember that all play is valid and important to the children, even when we can't see the point. This is a time for courtesy and respect – 'Please wait for me', 'Thank you for giving me your cushion'.

Try to avoid too many bumps and bruises. Childhood can be so painful, and pinched fingers, banged heads and grazed knees contribute nothing to your mutual pleasure.

You will become gradually more workmanlike at guiding her through the themes. Don't look for instant results. You are not trying to teach her tricks. There will be a steady growth in strength, skill and confidence.

Give her your complete attention and be sure that she is happy. Children love gentle teasing, 'in-jokes' and silly words, and recognize repeated phrases – 'Come on little bossy boots', 'Move your floppy froggy legs', 'One, two, I'm bigger than you. Two, three, you're bigger than me'. You may find it silly, but she will adore it.

Aim to have at least two half-hour 'class times' a week. The ideas and shapes are not absolute in any way. They can be followed or simply used as a trigger for your own ideas. Everything you do applies to the rest of everyday life – you can take the fitness themes into the park for example.

Children often show a touching pleasure in their 'class time', a time of real joy and shared delight.

Movement is what children love most. It brings a kind of ecstasy, a special kind of happiness, that perhaps only the very young can feel.

7 GETTING READY

Children love rituals. Even when very young, children recognize the preparation for class – open the window for some fresh air. The room needs to be warm, clean and tidy. Think about safety.

First find the time! No telephone, no chats – it is a real betrayal to interrupt and spoil the time. Clothes must be extremely comfortable – the lightest nappy, shorts or knickers will do. Chat as you take off your shoes together.

Talk about 'our class time' in a way she will understand – 'Shall we play our music?', 'Shall we dance together?' (See Page 19.) Allow her to help with clearing the space – she will bustle round pushing furniture (good for strength and learning about what will fit where). She will be helping you and making minute adjustments of co-ordination and muscular effort.

You need a 'safe' area in which anything valuable is out of range and where nothing can poke into eyes or

stub toes. Sometimes a teddy or doll has to be dressed too − Pobs was adamant about what she called 'decent clothes' for Mrs Honey, who was dressed (very good practice for small fingers), and who then watched or joined in as Pobs decided.

Make her feel that this is fun for you too − and be keen to begin. Try not to be side-tracked, and be fairly insistent about starting, even if you begin alone.

Start with 10 minutes only in mind. Don't watch the clock, and if it is a new experience, give her time to get used to seeing you prancing about.

◆ We have an old log basket in which we keep the 'gear' for class. It means that everything is there and you don't have to waste time finding things. It also makes an excellent house, kennel, flying balloon, or receptacle for balls or skittles.

◆ Make a tape or have some music handy that you both enjoy. Warm up to something jolly, such as Scottish dance music or anything in the 'Pops'. You don't need music for the rest, except as a perk-up if spirits sag or simply if you both enjoy it.

◆ Other useful items include ball and balloons, small towel, skittles or hoops and cushions.

8 WARM-UP

Bodies work best when they are warm. Muscles become more elastic and less likely to pull, and joints become more flexible. Children need very little warm-up time, but make quite sure that you are ready. You need time to find your energy and to get in the mood.

Put on some up-beat music you both enjoy. These are some ideas to get you dancing. You will need to adjust them to fit in with what appeals to your child.

Hold hands facing one another, pick up your feet in time to the music – heavy feet and light feet. Clap the beat and 'sing' the tune if you like, to stimulate breathing.

Alternate claps and stamps – rhythm is a great motivator – take turns to clap or stamp. Older children can do quite elaborate 'question and answer' patterns. (See page 91.)

PUNCHES

Punch the air around you, warming
your upper body. 'Shadow box' if
you like, and aim the punches into
the floor, walls or ceiling to change
the level and direction.

WALKABOUT

Hold hands and go on a 'walkabout'
– do big steps, little steps, stamps
and tippy-toes, fast and slow. Talk
about the 'space' you have – we call
this 'exploring the space' and 'know-
ing where you are in space'.
*Understanding this space around you is
an immense source of confidence and ease.*
Matching the size and strength of
your movements with the immediate
area is something of an art, and an
important safety factor. We all know
about the proverbial bull in a china
shop. 'Beat the bounds' by marking
the outer edges, touching the walls,
table, etc – 'This is as far as we can
go'. Run into the middle – 'This is
our spot in the middle', 'This is our
place by the window, door, etc',
'This is the corner – you stamp in
one corner and then we'll change
over', 'Stand in front of me,
behind, at the side...facing...or
back to back...'.

down on the floor. Hold her hands and let her do the work. It is all to do with 'getting ecstatic' and we call it 'swinging out'. Anything done on the floor – crawling, rolling, 'swimming' – calms them, and they settle very quickly.

HIGH JUMPS

When they are still small enough, they love to be 'jumped' and lifted. It is hard work and very 'warming'.

ROOTS

Bending your knees, 'feel' the floor. We call this 'putting down roots', and looking for earth energy. Pull up into a stretch – 'Up into the sky'. Children move up and down at giddying speed – 'You can go fast and I'll go slowly' is the way round that one.

If at any time the child is getting a bit over-excited and wild, *always* sit

Stand her on a chair to make the lift easier, and bounce – if the chair can stand it. Always bend your knees to lift a child, and keep the tummy, back and buttocks firm, to avoid over-taxing your back.

When they are older, skip, jump and spring together. Feel like a bouncing ball – jumps can be two feet together, two feet to one foot, one foot to two feet, or hopping on one foot and then the other. Gallop and spring with knees higher, or scissor-jump – they love having a shot at a jump and are quite happy with their own variations. Practise in the park or anywhere out of doors.

Springing, apart from being extremely warming and strengthening, is a compulsive human activity. Sing all the old rhymes you can remember – Ride a cock horse, Jack be nimble/Jack be quick/Jack jump over the candlestick. Make up some rhymes and chant together:

I'm like a great big bouncing ball,
High in the air, then down I fall
I bounce in and out,
And I bounce all around,
Then with a 'swish', I roll on the ground.

Not exactly poetry, but they love it. Any fast beat music has them leaping around.

OVER THE WAVES

In these two pictures Lala is swinging Pobs through her knees and up into the air. This takes a little 'managing'. We call it 'over the waves' as it reminds me of being swung up over the waves at the seaside as a child. You need to be strong and very rhythmical in the swinging. It is enormous fun for the child and will leave you both warm and exhilarated. Sometimes class simply stops here.

Some children, by the time they get

to four, can be very strong and bois-terous. You must insist on their using the space sensibly and not bumping into you. It sometimes helps to let them out to run to the landing or

down the passage and back, or even to do your warm-up by running in the park.

'Understanding' directions, judging distance and manoeuvring within a space, have to be learned and prac-tised like driving a car. It is the first safety factor and a major help in preventing falls and collisions. Talk about the directions in which you can move: forwards, backwards, sideways, into the corner, across the room or corner to corner (on the diagonal). Walk around me and cross over with me ('dozie do'). Skip, step or run the patterns with some music. 'Walk to meet me – now walk away backwards. Move round in a circle – "Ring o' Roses".'

We have a little rhyme:

I walk forwards,
I walk back,
I stretch upwards, I stretch down,
I turn on my toes,
And run all round the town

Take turns if you are too puffed. You should now be warm and ani-mated and ready to stretch. Any of these ideas can be used for teaching. Children cannot cope with the strain of adult 'stamina' aerobics, and can perform only short bursts of high energy work. For your own stamina, you need to fill the exercises out to suit yourself.

9 STRETCH

One awkward thing about coping with small children is that you feel as if you are leaning over all the time adjusting to their height. I remember my children being given yo-yos and feeling I'd spent the whole summer crouched double like an ancient crone untangling the strings. If you can, sit down or even kneel to talk, brush hair or dress them. It does help. Try to remember to straighten up your back constantly. Free your neck by balancing your head and turning it gently from side to side, opening your mouth to release the back of the neck.

POSTURE CHECK

Check your posture in the mirror. Hands on the top of your head, shoulders dropped and level, hips level. Nursing a baby and carrying a toddler on your hip is disastrous for your posture. If you have not recovered your tummy muscles after a pregnancy, you can very easily set up serious problems for your lower back.

Muscles when not in use tend to shorten or shrink slightly. (See page 24.) This sets up a tension on the joints and they become slightly misaligned. We stretch instinctively to realign the joints by pulling out the muscles. Tiny babies stretch and yawn; children, while playing, stretch and reach out constantly. When the scale of everything is too big for them, you could say that their whole life is 'one long stretch'.

They do not need to set up and practise specific stretches as much as an adult. They don't have the muscle bulk to sustain or hold them and will flop down just as you are beginning to enjoy the benefit. Under-threes can stretch out more easily along the floor.

WHOLE BODY STRETCHES

Lie on your tummies, facing each other. Stretch out to touch fingertips, then roll on to one side and stretch

swivel around, run about and come back.

After your warm-up do some 'sky stretches' – 'Reach for the sky...you're nearly as big as I am... stretch your feet'. They will try several little quick stretches to your one long stretch.

LEG STRETCHES

Sit on the floor and stretch out your legs. Lean forward. 'Can you tap your toes? Can you stretch them wide apart?' Toes stretched and then toes up. Small children can't lift their legs easily, but they love to try – Pobs is having a go at stretching her hamstrings. You can gently support and stretch the leg. They usually roll backwards to 'accommodate' the stretch, and instinctively avoid straining their backs.

the other. Roll on to your back and try to touch. Make it very playful – 'I'm going to catch your hands... head... feet'. They will probably

ENERGY STRETCHES

Put her on your lap and stretch her legs upwards or outwards. Roll back gently – on to cushions if you like – feet up in the air. 'Swish' up again. As they grow, they like to do this by themselves.

Be careful not to cramp her neck. You will find this rocking gives you lots of energy and it always makes children laugh. It is good for lymphatic 'drainage' of your legs and for stimulating the circulation, quite apart from releasing tension in the hips and pelvis.

Lie on your back kicking and stretching your legs – riding bicycles, 'snip-snap scissors' (legs out to the sides and in), and 'frog's legs' (bend and stretch the legs with the knees facing outwards).

UPSIDE-DOWN STRETCHES

Children love being tipped upside down. The world looks different, and it stretches their spines in perfect alignment. If they are light enough, start by sitting them on your lap facing outwards and saying a little rhyme:

> *Leg over, leg over*
>> (stretch and cross their legs)
> *As the dog went to Dover,*
> *He came to a stile*
>> (hold above the knees)
> *And whoops he went over.*
>> (lift them upwards and over)

Pobs enjoyed being held upside-down by her ankles even as a very small baby. You need to be sensitive to what they can manage and be careful not to jolt or alarm them.

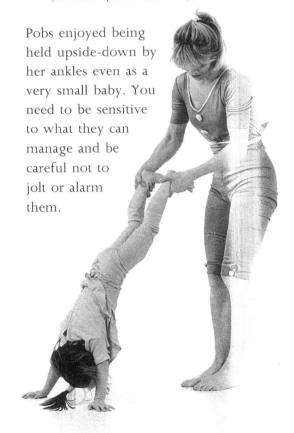

Children are total survival experts and never repeat anything that hurts or frightens them. Make sure you tuck in their heads if they roll over.

Pobs is trying a 'hand stand' stretch. Lala is supporting her weight and she will tuck in her head and be rolled over gently. This is easier to manage when they grow too heavy to hold them hanging upside down.

REACHING OUT

Children naturally reach out to touch things. Any variations such as 'tap my head' or 'reach this ball', can be tried. Kneeling down means you can stretch too. These stretches release the upper back, arms and shoulders.

SIDE STRETCHES

Pobs is having a shot at some side twists and stretches by swinging the skittles up and down. It can be difficult to balance, and you will need to work round your child and fit in your own side stretches. You vitally need the antidote to all the inevitable stooping, carrying and lifting you do. You must re-establish your body limits, i.e. how far you can reach, and feel 'released' to move freely 'in space'.

Stretching, as we have seen, is not a real problem for children. Even their posture at this stage is affected more by strength and confidence than by the need to realign their bodies through stretching.

10 STRENGTH

It is curious that muscular strength seems, even in young babies, to vary considerably. Some, almost immediately, arch their backs and try to lift their heads, kicking hard with stout little legs. Others, though equally healthy, feel far more floppy and less physically active.

Strengthening and toning the muscles is an important part of fitness. It involves the large muscle groups in the back, tummy, thighs and buttocks. It prepares them for games, gymnastics, sport and athletics when they go to school.

Muscular endurance, which involves repetitions of the same movement, is difficult for children to achieve. They simply do not have the necessary muscle 'bulk' to sustain repetition. It is, as we have explained, quite contrary to their nature (see page 35) and could, if forced, damage their bone structure.

There are three easy ways to increase muscular strength in children, which they instinctively practise. All the big muscle groups are involved as children's bodies do not work in isolated muscle groups.
◆ Contracting 'inwards', i.e. squeezing, hugging, 'hanging on'.
◆ Lifting the body weight, i.e. climbing, jumping or holding a balance position.
◆ Contra-movements (working against an outside force), i.e. pushing, pulling, heaving and carrying.

Some small children love to 'toil' and will pitch themselves into weight work like a cavalry charge. My son Julian moved furniture for years, often barricading himself in quite by mistake. We had to call instructions to him through the door to help him escape.

They need to reach the limit of their strength in order to increase and build it up rather like any sport training. Children are often 'at odds' over misjudging the degree of strength required for a given task. Only constant practice teaches them to match intention with effort. A vase of flowers requires a lighter push to move it than an arm chair. Hold the pussy cat gently, does not mean squeeze her. We call it 'misplacing the effort'.

LEARNING ABOUT STRENGTH

Strength work has enormous psychological implications. We talk of 'earth energy' and feeling strong and rooted. It helps the more timid child to stand his or her ground more effectively and become more confident. The more robust children learn that being strong does not mean being aggressive. Recognizing and accepting the limits of your own strength, and respecting other people's space is best learnt through play. Scrambling and wrestling are fun and must not end in tears. It also allows 'legitimate' aggression and letting off steam, without being a bully.

Small children take great pride in measuring their increasing strength.

'I couldn't carry this basket before...now I can'.

Strength is an essential safety factor. Strong bodies are less prone to exhaustion, stress and accident. Making correct judgements about space and effort builds confidence and a valuable sense of responsibility and control.

Lala and Pobs have cleared the space together, involving pushing and lifting. Children, unlike adults, never overstrain themselves. They have instinctively correct body alignment and use every ounce of strength – absolute 'whole body movement'. They also know exactly when to stop.

In working together, you will be toning, shaping and strengthening your body.

FIRM AS A ROCK
Kneel down and tighten your muscles, pulling in your tummy and feeling rooted to the ground. Be keenly aware of keeping your tummy and

back firm. 'See if you can make me move – come on, push – harder – try the other side – now push my shoulders.'

TREE TRUNK

'Now you stand firm like a tree and I'll see if I can make you move'. Try pushing her with your hands first, so that she gets the idea. Start by placing your feet at her hip level. 'Can you hold my legs up?' Put one foot on her shoulder, then the other. 'Can you hold me up?...Hold tightly, while I see if I can make you move.' Keep your tummy and buttocks firm to support your legs. It must be jokey – do not worry her in any way or make her feel uncomfortable and overloaded.

TUGGA-TOWEL

'Let's have a tug-of-war with this towel...heave, ho, off we go.' Rock backwards and forwards, pulling against one another. Face outwards and pull away. Flap the towel up and down and make a 'breeze' with it. 'Now let go and I'll flap it about...you try, and cool me down.' Use your whole back strongly. Hold the towel at each end, making a loop. Stand firmly based, feet apart and knees slightly bent, and say, 'Hold on, pick up your legs and we'll see if I can lift you up', or

catch her round the middle with the towel and 'Let's see if you can struggle away'. Then see if you can wring it out, she can twist one end and you can twist the other...'Come on, help'...and then, 'Let's whack the ground, thump, thump, and get really cross'. Some more timid children find it difficult to express any sort of aggression. This sort of play is extremely valuable in teaching them how to do so.

SQUIDGE BALL

A 'squidge' ball or a cushion is an excellent prop. Few children can resist a ball made of soft but strong sponge (the cover is tough PVC), and it is suitable for indoors, although it is not safe for unsupervised play. Pieces can be gouged out with scissors or a knife, and the sponge is dangerous if swallowed. One of our puppies shredded one once, which alarmed me considerably.

'Lie on top of the ball and hide it from me. Hold on tightly while I see if I can get it away from you. I'll roll you over and you hang on tightly. Now squeeze it with your knees – feet – hands. Let's see if we can flatten the ball. Sit on it – I'll hold it and you can lift up your feet.'

'Squash it with your hands – come on, push.' Note how Pobs has instinctively lifted her whole body to increase the weight.

Hold the ball between your knees and, holding her hands, let her stand on the ball, 'treading grapes', and pushing down strongly. Tell her to squeeze it down with her elbow, finger, head or knee...to push the ball against the wall, to lean on it, to put it behind her back and push hard. Do the same with her bottom.

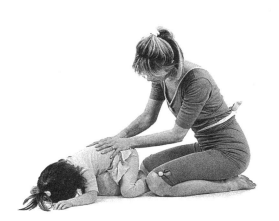

PUSH-ME-PULL-YOU

Children love mock battles –
contained 'ritual' aggression – and to
push and pull as hard as they can.
Sit or kneel, and start with hands on
shoulders. Are you ready? Take the
strain, now go! Push and pull, rock
sideways. Try to push one another
down. By four they enjoy proper
'bouts' with shoulders on the floor to
begin again. They will have great fun
mock-fighting their friends. If anyone
gets cross, stop at once. It must be
fun – 'If you are too rough, I won't
wrestle with you'.

Anything which encourages a child
to 'feel' her body weight is very
strengthening: Climbing up onto a
chair (see page 29), pulling up onto a
wall, climbing stairs, pushing up their
bottoms on all fours, and even holding
up a leg. They love holding on to
your hands and 'balance-walking' on
your feet.

FALLING TREES

We play something called 'falling
trees' which requires keeping a firm
back and legs. Stand with your feet
apart, hold her hands facing you,
her feet together 'as strong as a
tree'. Then ease her down sideways
to the ground and turn her over on
to her tummy.

See if she can lift up onto her arms
like a mini press-up. Lift her feet up
horizontally, but not if her back sags.
Lower her down, roll her over on to
her back again and, holding her
hands, heave her up in 'one piece'
into standing. To 'hold firm' is a
great strengthening effort for a child.

They become delighted with themselves and positively purr. I am sure
that one day some interesting work
will be done on the positive psychological effects of such 'weight work'.

You will notice a great increase in
your own strength and general muscle tone in your back, tummy,
buttocks and thighs. There will be
some psychological spin-offs and
release of tension in you too.

11 MOBILITY

Mobility is about keeping the joints supple. Rather like stretching, it is not only a fun game for children. Their joints are soft and mobile, held in place by relatively strong ligaments. (See page 00.) With all the stooping, lifting and carrying involved with childcare, you are the one who may start to feel strained and stiff. It is of paramount importance to keep your joints supple.

It is interesting to watch children flop out on the floor. They seem to flatten out completely, and almost 'melt', with no tension in the joints at all. When some children are resting, they enjoy having their legs, knees, feet and backs gently mas-saged. In my experience, however, some children dislike it and will protest. Use the time in this case to flatten out and align your back on the floor and yawn and relax.

EASE OUT YOUR BACK

Sit on the floor facing each other, cross-legged or feet together and knees pressed outwards. Your spine will be stable and you can safely tilt forwards, gently easing out your lower back. This is absolutely essential exercise and a great antidote to backache. It is a useful time to teach 'body awareness'. Very young children love to point to eyes, noses, and hair, but as they grow older the bones and joints take priority. Shins, heels, knees and ribs become

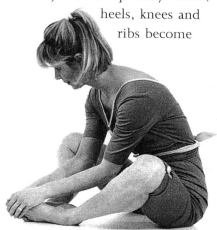

fascinating – 'Can you feel my elbow?'

Play a little game, moving all the joints and discovering how they work – they will need to copy you to begin with. They won't do any large movements. As with stretching, the movements are quick and light, but you can work down the body.

Open your mouth –
'This is my jaw.'

Pretend to chew and snap your teeth.

Nod – 'Yes, yes, I can turn my head.'

Arch your back and ease out – 'Can you shake your back and shoulders like a wet dog?'

Lean forward – 'Put your nose on the ground and spot a daisy.'

Straighten up and lean back – 'Spot a star.' Bend elbows and waggle your shoulders up and down – 'Can you cluck like a hen or fly like a bird?'

Bend and stretch your knees and elbows – 'Let's make our knees and elbows do chuffa, chuffa train...chuff, chuff, chuff.'

'Twisties' – 'Shall we do our twisties? Twist around and touch the floor behind you, right around. Now with the other hand.'

Put your legs out straight, twisting from the hip – 'Can you make your foot, then your ankle, then your whole leg, go round?'

Put your arms out, twisting from the shoulder – 'Can you make your hands go round, now your elbow, now your whole arm.' (Say it in the rhythm of 'ready, steady, go!')

We play a mobility game, sung to the tune of 'Hokey-Cokey'. It doesn't have to rhyme. Just make it up as you go along. Four-to-fives love 'impossible' tasks such as 'put your elbow on your heel' and will laugh and fall about. It goes like this:

Put your hands on your head,
Now the back of your neck,
Put your hands on your shoulders,
Now right behind your back,
Do the hokey-cokey, turn yourself around,
That's what it's all about.
Put your elbow on your knee,
Now stick it in your ribs,
Put your elbow on your hip,
And right up on your ear,
Do the hokey-cokey, wave it all around,
That's what it's all about.
Put your heel on your shin,
Now right up on your knee,
Put your heel on your tum,
Then right behind your bum,
Do the hokey-cokey, shake it up and down,
That's what it's all about.

Now it's your turn – they will make extravagant demands that you won't manage at all.

Clever Hands And Feet

Small children love their hands and feet. Babies are so much less 'bored' when they have discovered their fingers and toes and will play happily, catching and chewing. To begin with, hands and feet work as a foursome, and even up to three years it is difficult to work hands and feet one at a time. You can play hands and finger games at any time and they are ideal for car journeys. There is an excellent book of games – Finger Games – but very simply, and with any variation you like, mobilize your wrists, hands and fingers. (See page 115.)

'Show me your hands – now your palms, now back again.

Open your fingers, peep through them – twinkle them like stars.

Snip, snip scissors...make a fist...make a flat fish.

Waggle your fingers – and make them dance, walk them and run them along the ground. Can they meet each other in the air?

Clap – Clap – Clap – Clap.'

Stay Friends with Your Feet

Feet are a miracle of engineering. They affect everything about us, from our posture to our feelings of confidence and well-being. If our feet our miserable, nothing about us is right.

Feet need firm ground to strengthen muscles, so children should be barefoot as much as possible.

Pobs and Lala have been talking about feet, and are pulling up their toes, stretching the backs of their ankles.

Point your toes, then push down your heels. Say the rhyme and act it out:

My feet are my best friends
They carry me around
For I can run and walk and skip
And jump upon the ground

'Can your feet do all the things your clever hands do? – Not quite'. Persuade her to sit down again if you can. Point out the soles of her feet – 'It's tickly like the palm of your hand – and the five toes are like five little fingers. My foot is large, yours is little,

wiggle yours about, clap/stamp your feet, pretend to make a footprint by pressing down. Make your toes run, now your heels, now big flat feet'.

Talking about feet usually makes children run about. Keep sitting down if you can as it relieves the pressure on the small joints in the feet. Have your knees up under your chin, and change the effort (dynamics) and pace of the stepping as you move your feet up and down. Thus:

> *Here come my slippers.* (light steps)
> *Here come my shoes.* (firmer steps)
> *Here come my great big wellington boots.*
> (big slow steps)
> *Here come the buttercups.*
> *Here are the birds.*
> *Here come the flip, flop puddle-ducks.*

Staying friends with your feet makes a good rule for life. As with babies, you can massage your child's feet (and your own), cupping and rubbing around the heels and gently manipulating the toes.

SPECIALLY FOR BACKS

Keeping the back strong and supple is essential to relieve tension and exhaustion for both of you. Children love curling their backs. When they are tired, it helps to lie them down and gently push the knees upwards.

LOWER BACK
Pobs is holding the squidge ball and Lala is gently pushing up her feet and stretching her lower back. You can do the same. You need to feel your spine lengthening like a fox's tail.

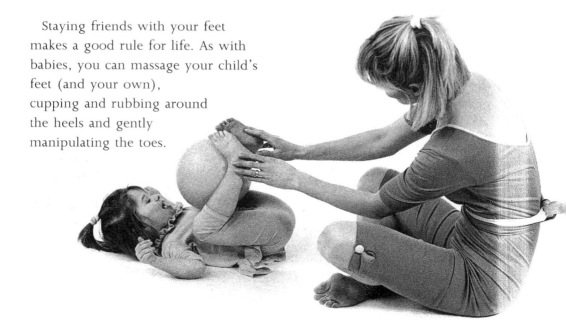

'Rolling' out your back very slowly, one vertebra at a time, is the best way to keep it supple. You can have fun together. Either sitting on your lap or beside you, ease out slowly, saying:

I'm a jelly, I'm a jelly.
(Sliding backwards to the floor)
I'm a jam roly-poly.
(Rock from side to side)

You can put cushions behind you and tip up more quickly – feet in the air – but be careful if you have her on your lap not to squash her neck. Children very quickly like to do the action rhythm by themselves and roll over and over on the floor.

STRONG STRETCH

'Make a tent'. This is a favourite stretch on all fours and one of those strange spontaneous movement patterns that suddenly 'appears'. Starting from sitting, the child pushes forward, stretching legs and back 'like a tent'. It is a preparation for a head-over-heels or hand- stand. They enjoy the upside-down view of the world.

12 FUN STUNTS

Children love stunts. Most of us have ecstatic memories of being lifted and swung through the air, jumping down off a high wall or riding our bikes with no hands. The excitement and rush of adrenalin, the thrill of screwing up your courage that it brings, remains a key motivation in many people's lives. Pushing ourselves to the limits is a human compulsion. How fast can I run? How high can I fly? How much can I lift? — is but the physical manifestation of that questing ambition that sends people across seas and out into space.

This may be an exaggeration when applied to 'Fun Stunts' for children, but the concentration and sense of achievement, the increase in confidence and ability to assess and tackle a difficult situation, is a valuable part of growing up. It is also a time for trusting and relying on one another, which builds admiration and respect. This is no small thing when the inevitable conflicts of adolescence begin.

SAFE SPACE

You need a safe space where heads can't be bumped. 'Soft' floors are best, and a carpet or gym mat make it easier for your back and knees. Never attempt anything that you find physically difficult. Say 'We'll leave that for John — he's stronger than I am'. There must not be any falls. They hurt and are counter-productive. You are trying to build confidence and sensible judgement about safety. Stay well within your limits.

I'm always slightly baffled at the way children enjoy stunts. Even the most timid glow with pride over the most modest 'tricks'. Measuring themselves against earlier achievements, they say, 'I couldn't do that before you know...look now.'

Because you need to work together rhythmically, it can be fun to attach little rhymes to what you're doing. Or you can simply count or allow time to feel your way at first. You would at least be sure of starting together. In using your child's body weight, you will be toning and tightening your own muscles.

THE ROLLERCOASTER

Children delight in the thrill of the rollercoaster drop – 'leaving your tummy behind'. (See page 27.) When she gets too heavy, jump her off an arm chair. You can lift her up over your shoulder into a 'fireman's lift' across your back. Hold her knees, then feet, and lean forward as she hangs down your back. Either retrieve her back over your shoulder, or kneel down and deposit her back on to the chair, bottom first. *Move very slowly, and tell her exactly what to do.* She will probably want to crawl down your back and slide on to the floor when you kneel down. Accept any suggestions and see if they work. You can say as you put her down:

1, 2, 3 – I drop down to my knee...
2, 3, 4 – I drop down on to the floor...

Roll her on to the floor very gently.

It always seems that no sooner do children get up and walk, than a new crawling phase appears, but on straight legs. They love to tip forward and look through their feet, stretching arms and legs. This strengthens and stretches their legs and backs and is the preparation for head-over-heels, cartwheels, headstands and the more advanced back flips or rolls of the school gym. Pobs has moved from the 'tent stretch' (see page 61) into walking on all fours 'like a camel'. Keep your knees bent if you have to join in. It is quite an awkward angle for an adult.

Suggest other ideas. Walk sideways (like a crab), round and round (spinning top), with your knees out (frog hops), or feet up to hands (bunny hops). There is a special technique for learning head-over-heels, which children love. You need to be very careful of her neck. It can be useful to start on a bed. Stand beside the bed or kneel beside her on the floor. Place your forearm under her hips to support her, tuck in her head with the other hand and, controlling her all the way, turn her over. It helps to place a cushion under her back.

In the same way, but always supporting her back, she can do a 'pretend' handstand, straightening her legs in the air. On a bed or large cushion, pull her up gently by her ankles (knees to start with). Let her hang, then put her down on her tummy or, if she can, tuck in her head and turn her over on to her back.

Some children love being swung, gently tapping the floor or bed with their fingers. If they are tired it can be very refreshing. (See page 50.)

I'm a little hat,
Swinging upside down,
I stretch my hands,
And touch the ground.

'SHAKE A MONKEY'.

This is one way to improve your pelvic tilt. Sit on the floor with your knees bent or with crossed legs. Get her to climb on to your back and hold

tightly with her arms and legs while you see if you can shake her off. If you are on a bed or soft surface you can be quite rough and she can roll off – 'I'm shaking a monkey off my back, flick-flack, flick-flack' – but hold on to her hands if she is worried. You can do this as a piggy-back ride, where she can learn to cling on without help while you prance about. Be ready to catch her as children often mysteriously let go. They do not have the muscle bulk to sustain the grip for very long.

FLYING BIRD

You can follow this climbing up idea with a variation, which is also good for your buttocks and legs.

Sit on your knees, and as she clambers up, tip forwards and see

if she can balance – 'Can you lift up your arms and legs like a flying bird?'

As they grow, they can sit up and ride on your back, turn round and ride facing backwards, as you walk on all fours like an elephant.

If someone else is around to steady her, she can even get up first on to her knees and then into a standing position.

'UP AND OVERS'

(See note on lifting, page 46.)

These are a time-honoured and much-loved 'stunt'. The idea is that they walk up on to your knees and then tip over backwards.

Pobs is doing the 'advanced' version, holding hands. As an easier way you can hold your child under her arms to help her climb up to balance on your knees. This is a stunt in itself.

Hold her against your tummy, her legs on either side.

Tip her up by bending forward

holding her against you – another stunt for tinies, supporting her back and head.

Hold the top of her arms to turn her over.

*I'm climbing up the
mountain,
I'll get there soon,
I tip upside down,
And fly to the moon.*

*Stop at any stage if
she is alarmed,
and she will
naturally
progress at her own
speed.* Finish the stunt at any point, twirl round holding her close for the 'finale'.

BALANCING TRICKS

Standing and walking unaided is a major balancing feat. The problem is that babies' heads are relatively heavy and they tip over very easily. They need to be encouraged to practise balancing, but always with supervision to avoid accidents. They need to learn to control their body weight and recover from a trip-up efficiently. Start by walking on an 'uneven' surface. Put some

cushions on the floor and see if she can step on and off them without tripping. Bounce and walk about on a bed or sofa. Try walking in a line on the carpet. Practise along the garden wall, and let her stand up on your shoulders or knees. Small children have an almost suicidal attraction to stairs, and they love to learn to negotiate them. But this requires extremely careful supervision. Every climb onto a chair, table or wall should end in a held balance with arms out. Say:

*1,2,3 – Look at me!
I'm so high,
Up in the sky.
Will I fall?
No chance at all.*
Then swing her down.

She can progress to balancing on one leg or tipping forward into a mini-arabesque. Pobs is practising a balance on Lala's knees. Start with your knees straight. Hold her hips, slowly bend your knees. Then let go when she is ready. 'Steady now – one hand – look, no hands. Have you got the wibbly-wobbles?' Move your knees slightly, then, holding her under her arms, jump her down. This knee-balance can develop into other 'tricks'. Put her hands on your shoulders, lean forward, and she can slide down over your back. Or, with her hands on your shoulders, tip her legs up, holding her hips. She can then wave her legs – 'We're walking on air'.

'SWALLOW DIVE'

This is another favourite, with endless variations. Use her weight to tighten your thighs, buttocks and tummy. Lie on your back holding her hands. Press your feet against her body. Slowly and with lots of

encouragement, lift her up on your feet until she is horizontal. When she is steady in the 'horizontal balance' let go of her hands. Pobs can almost 'fly', but she is not yet strong enough to get her feet up in a 'dive'. Be ready to take her hands at any moment. Bend and stretch your knees – 'Steady, don't wriggle.' If you feel at all unsafe, make sure someone is with you to help support her.

An easier version is for her to rest on your shins. You can tip her forward as you pull your knees up. You'll soon be told 'too easy-peasy', but it's a good way to begin.

'Sky Lift'

Try this one only with another adult in case you tip sideways. Lie on your back, hold her hands and let her sit on the soles of your feet. Lift her slowly by pulling your knees up to your

chest, then straightening them upwards. She can hook her feet round your calves to sit firmly. With the support of another adult she could sit up straight to balance on your feet, or even stand up. This is pure circus and very challenging. Never attempt this alone with your child.

Rumble Tumble – Learning How To Fall

Pobs seemed to consider these were her 'best' tricks and she needed to put on her trainers. They were not necessary, but only fun.

Bend down on your hands and knees. This is good for pulling out and tightening your lower back and knees. Sit high enough to make it a real effort for her to climb up. When she gets

on her own yet. Older children love to tuck in their heads and do a flashy head-over-heels and a roll.

When I was a child, we used to climb over the back of an old arm-chair, slide down towards the seat, tuck in our heads, roll over and leap on to our feet, rather like the Cretan bull dancers. We could also roll over sideways across the arms and jump onto the floor. This is excellent preparation for gym at school and is enormous fun.

COMBINING STRENGTH AND BALANCE

'HEAVE A SACK OF SAND'

Children love being 'man-handled', and even babies enjoy being tipped over your back or across your knee. It is very strengthening for you and the game is that you don't get stuck anywhere. Your child has to adjust her weight continually, moving her arms and legs if you change your grip, tucking in when she's turning over and avoiding making uncon-trolled jerky movements. It's a wonderful exercise in muscular con-trol – 'Hold tight, don't flap about' – and you can do it with a partner, passing the child across or even sit-ting on a sofa. It reminds me of watching a long-suffering mother cat

there, shake or vibrate a little and say 'Tumble, tumble, tumble down'. Bend down low, so that she can do a 'con-trolled fall', easing out on to the floor and rolling over. You can practise this over a pile of cushions or bean bags. Pobs can't manage a head-over-heels

with three small kittens. When the clambering got too much, she would sit up and stretch and they'd all slide down to the floor. Make for the nearest chair if you lose the rhythm and need to start again.

You don't need to work grimly at stunts. You can do them at any time, purely for fun. If you start when they are babies, your strength will increase with their weight. Children love it with a strange ecstasy. It involves mind and body – trust, respect and great sense of control. There are lasting memories of fun and laughing.

13   SKILLS

~~~

As a teacher, Hinrich Medau had plenty of 'hand apparatus' in the school gyms. There were very formal set ways of using it, with charts showing you how to skip with a rope, twiddle clubs, lift dumbbells and chase rolling hoops. He used to laugh and say the best work was done before and after class when he would bend the rules and allow the children to 'play' with the gym apparatus. They would produce far more interesting skill patterns when left to improvise for themselves.

Like all teachers, he appreciated that children are naturally fascinated by the outside world. Anything 'in scale', i.e. the right size for them, they will seize upon and try out all sorts of ideas quite instinctively. This is why toys which allow no element of improvisation, where everything is done for you – electronic cars and gadgets among them – have a limited educational value.

When your tiny baby watches a mobile swaying gently over her pram, or follows the sound of a rattle, we can see the first fascination with toys. They are delighted by things that move, and very early on they make little dabbing movements, 'patting' at rattles or even household spoons strung across their cots. We had a light ball suspended on a string which my children loved to pat. I'm sure a case could be made for learning to play tennis 'in your pram'!

All babies enjoy a variety of shapes and textures to handle and touch. The movements are fairly unfocussed to begin with, but once they can pat, grasp and then hold with two hands together, they are already becoming skilled 'sportspeople'.

It is fascinating that, like all patterns of development, new skills seem to appear as if from nowhere. Why does the block dropped on the floor suddenly become a missile zooming past your ear, accompanied by screams of delight? Children practise new skills almost obsessively. What begins as natural curiosity becomes a desire to control and manage cause and effect. 'What is that bright red ball?' becomes 'What will it do?', which then becomes 'What can I make it do?', and then leads to 'How can I do it better – harder – faster – more accurately?'

Some very small children show an astonishing aptitude in games of skill. Others – and Pobs is one – are less able. She says: 'I'm certainly not very good at tennis'. These children are happiest doing stunts and simply 'managing' their bodies. I always think it is the first separation of the dancers and gymnasts from the games players.

SQUIDGE BALL

Playing with a large soft ball is an excellent way to learn all the basic skills involved in games playing. There is a certain magic in a ball. It has an energy and life of its own. Pobs, like all children, loved the large yellow ball (see Baby Moves). It is safe indoors, i.e. it won't break the windows or damage the furniture, but can also bounce without the risk of jumping up too quickly and flattening noses. It is easy to grasp, and is light enough to be carried, while being heavy enough to catch, roll and retrieve. It is equally useful out of doors and appeals to children of all ages. (See note on safety, page 89.)

Here are some ideas on the way you might play 'squidge ball'. You need to adapt the play to suit the skill and interest levels of your child, who will probably take over anyway. I have written it as a conversation, and the movements are very recognizable (the aim of the movements is in brackets):

'Shall we get our squidge ball out of the box?

Can you carry it?

Drop it now and see if it rolls away. **(Timing and balance)**

Hold it up high first, and see if it will roll further.

Wait now till we count 'three'...
1, 2, 3...and drop.

Hold it on your head and drop it.

Let's sit on the floor and roll the ball to each other.

Not too hard – oh, that one petered out!

Aim it towards my hands. **(Aim and control of effort)**

See if you can stop it with your feet – you can kick.

I'll roll the squidge ball to you and you kick it back – oh, missed it! **(Kicking)**

Let's start with a kick this time.

Do you want to try by yourself?

May I join in?

There are lots of ways of kicking – look, with your toe, the side of your foot, backwards with your heel. **(Control with hands and feet)**

See if you can hold it with your hands, drop it and – quick – kick!

Let's kick it against the wall and watch it come back. **(Control and sharing an activity)**

Shall I have a turn?

Shall we try to kick it back – you are clever.

Wait, wait, my turn now.

Aim carefully. **(Speed and reaction time)**

Shall we do some footballing: not too rough till we go into the park.

Try not to bump me and mind the chair. **(Spatial awareness)**

Let's sit down now and squeeze the squidge ball, now pinch it with our fingers. This is the way that pussy cats sharpen their claws. **(Handling skill)**

Feel the smooth surface. Stroke it softly and push it over gently – rock, rock – can you make drumming rain drops with your fingers.

Now it's a wobbly jelly.

This is the thunder – boom, boom.

Hold the ball tightly and whack the floor.

Shall we do pat-a-cake – pat, pat – harder now, and see if you can make it jump.

Now that your hands are ready, let's see if we can throw and catch.

You throw first and I'll catch.

What a hard job – not so high this time – that's easier. **(Throwing and catching)**

You catch now.

Hold your hands up in front like

this, and I'll drop the ball into your arms.

Too late! – try again.

Now I'll stand a step away.

You're getting so good at catching, soon I'll do a big high throw for you to catch.

Shall we bounce it off the wall and see if we can catch it – let it bounce first.

Can you jump like the ball until it rolls away? **(Bouncing)**

Let's roll about when I do it again.

Can you bounce the squidge ball? It's quite big for you.

Hold it up and bounce...it will bounce a bit if you drop it, but will fly higher if you bounce hard. **(Cause and effect)**

When you are bigger, you'll be able to bounce and catch it or do lots of pat bounces, or bounce it high and clap your hands and run under it. Shall we see if we can throw the ball into the basket? **(Aiming and accuracy)**

You stand closer because I can reach further...

Thank you for the super game – you're getting so grown up and clever.'

These are only some ideas. It could take 10 minutes or a whole morning. Let your child set the pace. The ideas don't have to be in this sequence – the football could take over! You will find lots of combinations of movements and games for older children.

Try to put off competing for as long as you can. Answer the four-year old's persistent 'I'm better than you' with 'We're both good'. Little ones need constant encouragement and should never feel defeated. There should always be an enormous sense of achievement and fun. If you've ever heard football coaches talking, you will recognize the movement aims and skills in bold italics.

We try to keep the squidge balls for 'class time', but sometimes children quite desperately want to keep them around. I've known them to be walked solemnly in dollies' prams, comfortable on pillows and covered in blankets! In the face of such affection, it is best to go along with it and wait for the passion to pass.

'BREEZY B'LOONS'

It's fun to practise all the squidge ball skills with a balloon. You can do the same movements, but in a different dynamic, i.e. 'in lightness' and using vertical space, as we say. It is more difficult for a small child and demands enormous muscular control to adjust all the movements to such a light flyaway ball. They are called 'breezy b'loons'.

Some under-twos especially are afraid of the big bang if the balloon

pops. Don't blow them up too far, and talk about the 'big bang', clapping your hands together and going 'Bang' loudly. Make it a joke which you can share together. Encourage her to join in and shout 'Bang'. Some children hate noise and are distressed by cars hooting or street machines. It helps to practise making the noise yourself and treating it as a joke. There may be fewer tears on bonfire night.

Blow up the balloons together. See how light they are – 'We can blow hard and keep them in the air' – and then tap them lightly to keep them up, one hand and then the other. Run about with them – 'You hold yours

and I'll hold mine.' **(Breathing stimulation)**

'Which one would you like – green or blue? Would you mind if I had the green one?

Can you run on your toes? Sshhh – not like an elephant – lightly like the balloon, with little soft steps. **(Control and balance)**

Let's see if we can make the balloons stand upright on their balloon-sticks. They've only got one leg, so it's hard to balance. Quick – that one's falling – now that one. **(Strength and stretch)**

Let's toss it up in the air – stretch up high – toss it up again, and catch it with your fingertips.

Wait this time and catch it carefully, before it touches the ground. Hold your arms out carefully, just as you did with catching the ball. **(Catching)**

Can you toss it up with two arms together – don't fall over backwards will you? **(Aim)**

It won't land in the basket, as it keeps on floating away. (See Warm-up note on backs) Shall I swish you up 'over the waves' and see if you can kick the balloon up high...swish.

It's fun to have a 'grand finale', and if your child is light enough, and your back can stand it, she will adore the experience of swinging up and down. We were amused to discover that Pobs, who loves star jumps while being held upright, couldn't get her feet together in the air. If your child is older, let her climb up on to a chair and toss the balloon up high, before jumping down. Hold her hands and swing her down.

Co-ordination

These games of skill and co-ordination produce a strong and efficient little body. They use all the muscle groups, with many changes of direction and effort. They speed up their reaction time and improve all their travelling techniques, i.e. walking, running, jumping and skipping.

Children learn to make quick decisions or wait to see the result of their actions. They learn too the concept of gamesman-ship, to judge distance and to fit their movement into a space. They can accommodate another 'body' and enjoy playing together and adjusting to another's rhythm. They gauge how to get puffed and excited without losing control, to pace themselves. They enjoy the sense of achievement and 'measuring' their increasing skill. 'When I was lit-tle I couldn't do that, but when I'm bigger, I'll be able to.'

Games

By five, some children can be very strong and boisterous. Play the skill games outdoors if you can, or in the garage if it is a safe place. Balloons and balls can be thrown up in towels while you hold the corners. Goal posts can provide a more focussed game of throwing and kicking. Light bats and racquets extend the skill with smaller balls, and prepare them directly for bat-and-ball games. Hoops, skipping-ropes and coits

provide additional equipment. Try things out and see what works best. Attempt to be involved, even if you cheat a little. I've played many a game of football sitting on a garden chair.

They need to learn that games are games, to be played for fun. The timid child will gain confidence and the 'warlords' will settle down, play with more style, and do not have to win. In safety factor terms, learning to manage the environ-ment, understanding cause and effect, and improving co-ordination, cuts down the hazards of clumsiness. I think we often forget how painful childhood can be. If we pinched our fingers, bumped our heads, grazed our knees, fell off our bikes and then coped with the exhaustion of crying as often as children do, we'd see the necessity of 'practising co-ordination'.

Playing games is an excellent group activity which they love to organize themselves. You may need to do some 'sorting out', but it is useful for them to try. Attempt to arrange some allowances for the younger ones playing too. I spent my entire childhood trying to play cricket, tennis or darts with an older brother who used to mutter darkly: 'When are you going to get better at it?' I never did catch up.

14 HOOP-LA!

Children are great experts in producing the perfect work-out for themselves. Given an adaptable toy or piece of hand apparatus, they will work through the fitness factors – strength, stretch, suppleness and stamina – quite instinctively.

The hoop is an ideal trigger. Most toy shops have them, and the plastic ones are light and inexpensive. The 'magic circle' has enormous appeal to children of any age. These very versatile ideas could apply to almost anything you could find – a large ball, towel, or walking-stick. Under-twos will not achieve any real 'patterns' with the hoops, but they will find their own things to do.

Keep the hoops – two large and two small – with the other toys, specially for class, so that they do have some novelty value. 'Shall we do the

hoops today?' These ideas can happen in any order as children tend to take over anyway. Suggest a new theme only when their interest is flagging.

Run around with the hoop – don't bang it. **(Space)**

Roll the hoop and suggest catching it before it falls. Chase it together, see if you can roll it 'like this' – demonstrate. Hang it on your arm when you catch it. Catch it with two hands and drop it over your head.

'Let's hold it up and drop it – quick, pick it up again.'

Kneel down as the child stands. 'Hold it up as high as you can – a big, big stretch – now drop it.

We'll stretch our sides now – place the hoops together and twist over and back like a steering wheel. Look

through the hoop'. Sing together: 'The wheels of the bus go round and round...' Run about 'driving' the bus, twisting the hoop.

'Push your hoop against mine – you are strong – now pull them both together. Hold on tightly. Heave-ho, here we go...' Provide enough resistance for a real effort, strengthening your back at the same time. Children need to learn that strength does not mean aggression, and some children love bouts of strength and tussling.

'Let's make a door with the hoop – mind your head. I can't get through the little hoop, but you can. Can you crawl through/swim through/walk like a camel/go through backwards or sideways? (Usually bursts of running happen in between). Run around me and try this one...' This requires great control to slow down

in time to negotiate the hoop.

Make some extravagant suggestions.

Take turns – 'you hold it for me and I'll show you how to go through feet first/on my back/head first/on my tummy. **(Mobility)**

Let's put the hoops down – look, the small one fits inside the big one.

Is it a pool? Let's paddle our hands and feet'.

To ease out and rest the back, play a game mobilizing all the joints. Allow any suggestions – wriggling fingers and toes, putting your heads in 'to make your hair wet'. Children appreciate 'forbidden' suggestions in fantasy. 'Can you put first your elbows in, now one hand, now your bottom, now your chin?' You both need to move your body positions constantly.

It takes a bit of sorting out, and can become quite athletic: 'Let's jump into the "pool" we've made – splash!' Spring out and shake off the water. Jump in, sit down and roll or creep out sideways like a crab.

Let's play horse and cart. We'll take turns to be the horse...' Play some lively music and gallop about. Hold on opposite sides of the hoop – adult kneeling – and swing sideways:
'Swing high, swing low,
And over the rainbow.'

There are lots of energetic games – spin the hoop upright, run about and jump in where it falls.

Chasing and catching – hoop-la – using the hoop to 'tag', is a traditional favourite.

But chasing sometimes worries younger children as they are still hiding away and not at their 'hunting' stage yet. Push the hoop flat along the floor and say 'quick, run before it touches you...'

Kneel and stand inside the hoop together, pretending it is a rocking boat. Rock the boat:

Rock the boat
and we'll laugh and shout,
Rock the boat
Till we all fall out.
(Tip over sideways)

This sort of creative fitness play adjusts easily to younger and older groups. They will leave you in no doubt about what is 'too baby' or 'too difcoo' as Pobs says.

15 FLOPPING OUT

For a child, 'I'm so tired' means 'I need to rest, now'. Small children's energy patterns seem positively freakish to adults. Peaks of activity are followed by sudden and seemingly inexplicable exhaustion. If unable to rest at once, they become limp and tearful. We call it 'flopping out'.

As we have seen, it is the natural pattern for young bodies. After all, a herd of elephant moves no faster than the youngest baby in the group, and accommodates its frequent need for rest. A good deal of fretfulness in children is sheer exhaustion. They can't 'pace' themselves or hold anything in reserve.

They play to their maximum energy, and then quite suddenly have to stop.

I remember the wailing coming home from the park after too-long walks, festooned with bicycles and a dolly's pram dangling somewhere. I would stagger home, cross with everyone, saying 'You were all fine a moment ago' and 'I told you not to take that pram'. We all recognize this one, and also the speed with which they recover and want their tea, when you are still exhausted.

It does help to keep the push chair or buggy until it falls apart, and then replace it. Children should not walk for hours on hard pavements. No-one would dream of 'overwalking' a puppy, or be seen dragging it exhausted along the street. The quarrels and tears can be so easily avoided by a rest in the pram/buggy.

The 'worst' of children, I think, is that they are either too hot, too cold, too sticky or – as we have said – too tired. If you have a pram, a sweater, a drink and a wet sponge always on hand, the problems are very quickly cured.

You can expect a fair amount of flopping out during your 'class time'.

Go along with the changes of energy levels. Make the most of the peaks and sit out the pauses. Your ChildsPlay will be the one time when she can set the pace for herself, and discover intuitively how to arrange what suits her best.

It could be that without this they never feel quite at ease or recognize when things are right for them. It can't always be easy for children to manage a world which is not only permanently too big, but which also uses a quite different time scale totally opposed to their own.

16 A SPECIAL CASE FOR MOTHERS AND MINDERS

However great the long-term rewards, being responsible for small children can feel like total immersion. They never let up and you can sometimes wonder when it was that things felt really 'right' for you. Constantly adjusting to their needs can leave you feeling exasperated and quite unable to recognize yourself. Whatever happened to that chic, competent and clever lady? I remember saying once, when my twin sons were unruly four-year-olds: 'I was a really nice girl until I met you two. I never shouted or got cross.'

If you are doing well, and are perfectly happy, be glad and ignore the following chapter.

It can be a help to isolate the problems, and either give in graciously or try to avoid or 'cure' them.

'Do I like the new me?'
Accept that you won't be the same shape, and that you might well be more emotional and less in control.

Other relationships will seem different within the family. It's best to concentrate on first priorities, i.e. your own and your baby's well-being. Try not to fret and get too subtle about your relationships. You will all need warmth and affection at this stage and should trust to each other's best intentions. Do your post-natal energy programme (see pages 23–24) and you will steadily gather your strength.

'I'm a career woman really'
Children love routines and repetitions which can seem utterly boring. Sometimes sheer boredom can seem like exhaustion. If you are not naturally enchanted with baby clothes and small bodies, try to think that you are doing a 'job' that requires your best professional attention, your best performance. Think of your baby or child as an exciting project which demands all you can manage. It will ease the

'gear change' from professional woman to mother which, after all, is a proper job if ever there was one.

'My long-lost streamlined body'

When children are around, it seems like a never-ending picnic. I used to call it 'the bread and butter trail'. They eat little and take forever, and never seem to finish anything. It is difficult not to eat up the scraps in sheer frustration. This can be very fattening. Wiser to have a tin for the scraps for the bird table or for the ducks in the park, or a doggy bag for your own or your neighbour's dog. Pour the end of the fruit juices into a jug and use it later on.

'The day goes on forever'

Try to have a break from each other after lunch. It isn't always possible, but even half an hour relieves the pressure. We used to take to our beds and I valued this time enormously.

'There's so much strolling and sitting about'

Get up and play too. Try to get a little puffed every day – run, skip, play tag or jog with the push chair. Take a ball to the park and kick and throw it about. Pop a skipping-rope in your pocket and skip while you wait for the dawdlers to catch up.

THE MINI WORKOUT

I never do anything for myself'

Set up your scheme for a mini workout every day. If your baby watched your post-natal exercises, she will probably quite naturally join in. Start as soon as you feel comfortable. The exercises can be done alone, but Pobs joined in and was quite helpful and certainly full of advice. You may not work straight through them very often, but they are designed to be done separately to fit in with your busy life.

Have lots of cushions around to put under your head or lower back if it feels easier.

'My back aches here – in the hollow'

Such problem areas, after pregnancy, need special attention. Sit in front of a chair with your legs crossed. Lean forward, back straight,

pulling in your tummy strongly and pushing 'through' your knees. Hold for a count of 12.

Lean back slowly and put your weight on your hands. Pull in your tummy and carefully lift one foot and then the other up on to the chair. This position tilts the pelvis and you should feel the end of your spine lengthening. Hold for a count of 12. Pobs was being helpful holding Lala's feet. It turned into a game of catching feet up and under the chair.

'My posture is terrible and my neck is stiff'

Ease out your neck and shoulders. Necks tend to get stiff and shoulders hunch through carrying and constantly bending over small children. Lie back on the floor, with your legs and

feet vertical. Pobs sat on Lala's tummy to help flatten it. Put your arms out, elbows bent and hands behind your head. 'Melt' into the floor. Flatten out your upper back, tucking in your chin and lengthening the back of your neck. Turn your head slowly from side to side, releasing the neck and keeping your mouth open. Leaving your elbows flat, gently push your head up with your fingertips, tucking in your chin. Breathe out slowly and relax back on to the floor.

Yawn and stretch out your arms over your head wherever you please. Rest your feet on the chair and stretch again. Breathe freely.

'I need a half-size extra shoe'

Focus on your feet. Take off your shoes whenever you can. Rest your feet up high, wriggle your toes, and 'pump' your feet, pointing your toes and then pressing down your heels. This stimulates your circulation and lymphatic system. It is easier to do one leg at a time, resting the other on the chair. Pobs is keeping Lala's tummy flat here.

'I've put on weight around my thighs'

Tighten up your thighs. Lie flat, tucking in your chin. Have the chair handy to rest a leg when you need it. Press your heels towards the ceiling, one at a time if necessary. Squeeze your legs together strongly then, gripping the knees for support and keeping abdominals firm, push your feet apart slowly, keeping the legs tense. Pull them back together strongly, tightening your inner thigh muscles. Repeat 8 times slowly and 8 times quickly. Release tension in the feet by rotating them slowly. 'Shake out' your legs – put on some music and improvise anything you like ('Bicycling', 'Sky Stepping' and kicking are examples). When your back is supported, you are quite safe.

'I'm a different shape altogether'

Toning buttocks and tummy. Slide your lower legs up on to the chair. Squeezing the buttocks tightly together, lift the hips, pulling up the pelvic floor. Do not exaggerate your hollow back. Hold for a count of 8, then lower your hips very slowly. Change the pace into 8 short lifts, always controlling your weight as you return to the floor.

Leave one foot on the floor, with your knee bent for a variation. Try out other positions such as lifting one knee as you come up – Pobs enjoyed being tipped forward.

These are the big-time pull-ups and you need to start slowly. Start propped up on cushions, your feet on the chair. Breathing out and pulling in your tummy strongly, reach for your knees with your fingertips. Start with one hand out at a time, then reach across to the opposite knee. Don't struggle because your back muscles will take over. You need to strengthen your abdominals gradually. Roll out backwards and stretch whenever you feel the need. You can also begin with your legs under the chair. Bend your knees as you come up and hold on to the chair for support, pulling in your tummy as you breathe out. Achieving this position takes time and effort. Don't hurry – persuasion rather than attack is what flat tummies are about.

Pobs was not very pleased with her job of 'holding the chair steady'!

No small child can even begin to do these strong exercises. They do not have the muscle bulk. Once you know the positions, do them at any time – watching the television, talking on the phone or playing on the floor. You will very quickly notice the difference. Your muscles will be much firmer and your back will be stronger and safer.

Many women say that after the first campaign to shape up after the birth, their bodies seem stronger, more stable, and have an improved muscle tone. So take heart and give yourself time.

17 SOCIAL SKILLS FOR SOCIAL ANIMALS

In most of our lives, apart from the big tricks of fate, it is our human relationships which colour and influence us. We are instinctively social animals and need our 'pack', our network of relatives and friends, our place in the scheme of things. We cannot survive as lone bears in our separate caves.

Learning to get along with people, to grow as individuals within our group, and to make our best contribution, requires constant practice and experience. Communicating our own ideas, understanding other people's, making those minute unconscious adjustments to degrees of intimacy, are all social skills which require contact with a large and varied group.

It is difficult for children today to experience that variety. Families are smaller, they often split and regroup, the single parent is not unusual, and relatives often live separate lives at great distance and beyond regular

contact. People are more mobile, steady neighbourhood friends are fewer and tend to move on. No child ever talks to or smiles at a stranger — in a potentially dangerous world it is discouraged for their own safety.

Children today witness and receive a good deal of open — and covert — aggression. Rudeness and anger in the street is not unusual, hooting and cursing from car drivers an almost daily occurrence. Terrible scenes on the television make violence almost commonplace.

Nothing, except in very small communities, is conducive to the easy social interaction of children within the rest of a stressed, highly-paced society.

This is a relatively new state of affairs, and it is a great personal privation as I have always loved talking to children. One can scarcely smile at a baby in a pram without being mistaken for a child molester or baby snatcher.

We, as children, chatted to everyone, everywhere, asking questions and proffering information. We learned the small nuances of adult impatience – 'Right, that will do, off you go now' – in the kindest possible way. Our sympathy and interest was genuine, the contacts were real. Conversation was as natural as breathing. Even in the Sixties, my sons' favourite 'friend' was John, who swept the pavements. I remember their huge delight when he 'achieved' the new motorized barrow – 'It's his best thing, and he's frilled...'

It is easy today for small children to become 'isolated' within their own age group. 'They are so busy, they have more friends than we do', parents are fond of saying. It should be plain, however, that you do not learn a variety of social skills within your own peer group. Conversation and vocabulary are necessarily limited, and social interaction amongst a mob of toddlers can be something akin to jungle warfare. Being forced to 'share' and be 'good mixers' before they have developed a real sense of self can provoke hysterical screams of 'That's mine!' They certainly learn to fight.

Young children need a kindly adult with whom to rest, practise and learn. Friends are great, but it wasn't for nothing that one small boy said 'My best friends leave me alone'.

MAKING CONTACT

Pobs and Lala are chanting a little rhyme that children love. Sit down so that you are on her eye-level and show her carefully how to do the actions. This sort of play provides good practice at matching words, feelings and movement. It makes you smile and get each other in focus.

I like myself, (Pat your chest)
And I like you, (Pat each other's shoulders)
I'm pleased we're together, (Keep hands on shoulders...sway)
And how-do-you do. (Shake hands)
We've lots of things to say, (Hold hands, lean forwards so that your noses nearly meet)
And lots of things to do, (Clap hands)
For I like myself, (Pat your chest)
And I like you. (Big hug)

Try to change the pace of the words. For example, 'lots of things...' could be said more quickly, and the last line very slowly for emphasis.

'Just talk' – Words and Sentences

Babies love sounds. They follow a rattle or tinkling ball, respond to a soothing lullaby, smile when they recognize familiar voices. Experts say it is the rhythm of the sound that attracts them, e.g. 'Cuck-oo – Peek-a-boo – Cuck-oo', long before the meaning has any possible reference. We have a video film of Pobs at four months sitting on my knee playing 'This is the way the ladies ride'. She opens her eyes wide and hunches her shoulders for the galloping huntsmen. She knew exactly from the rhythm when to expect the big jumps.

By about four months, babies are making wonderful sounds, gurgling, smiling and saying 'a-goo, da-da'. It seems that it is your eyes to which they respond most. Talk to her as much as possible, sing, and say all the nursery-rhymes: Pat-a-cake, Humpty-Dumpty, Dance for your Daddy, Jack and Jill, especially if there are actions to match. There are masses of books to guide you. We all know the enchantment of that first wave, when 'bye-bye' actually means a wave of the hand – the magic link of word and response has been achieved.

Repeating songs and rhymes helps the rhythm of unbroken speech, and later, the mastery of properly constructed sentences. Describe what you have just been doing together so that she can join in, and tell her stories about people she knows. She will ask repeatedly for the same stories: 'Tell me about when you caught your knee in the gate'... You may think 'Oh – not again!', but she needs time to link the sense of the words with the story line, and then to absorb all the complexities of the meaning. Those terrible old jokes about how you stepped in a puddle or how the bus ran over your hat. She will love to laugh again and again.

Listen carefully when she talks, and never interrupt her. It takes time to think as you speak, and to relate an incident in correct time sequences. Argument and logic are sophisticated concepts, and exchanging ideas in words is a basic and vital skill of communication.

I did think at one time that my son James was going to stammer. On close watching, we discovered that he was being constantly interrupted by the other two and quite unable to get into the rhythm of longer sentences. 'Let James speak' became the cry. He very soon 'grew through it', and in a family of addicted talkers, he is by far the worst.

'You don't have to shout' – Pitching the Voice

Even when they know the words, it is difficult for children to get the voice quite right. Adult instructions veer from 'Speak up' to 'You don't have to shout!', 'Don't talk to me from the door', 'Don't pull my arm when you talk', and 'Don't breathe on my face'. Children's voices 'swing about'. There is the slow monotone when you are in a hurry and the metallic screech when you want them to speak quietly. There is any range of eccentric sounds in-between.

For her own safety, every child should be able to scream and shout. Find a practice time – on a beach, running the bath, or accompanied by loud music – and make all the loudest noises you can. It is wonderfully releasing and should be fun.

Even when you are trying, it is hard to 'pitch' your voice correctly and produce a sound that doesn't grate. Adults frequently get it wrong. The subtle changes of facial expression, the smiles and the eye contact are an integral part of sophisticated social interaction. Even judging the correct distance to stand when you speak can have a great influence on the outcome of a conversation. Being too far away seems unfriendly, being too close can seem over-familiar and uncomfortable.

THE VOICE GAME

Lala and Pobs are playing the 'Voice Game'. There are endless variations, the main idea being to teach your child to listen, to judge distance, to follow sounds (a major safety factor in crossing roads) and to pitch her voice correctly. Say 'I'll close my eyes and you walk round me. Stand still and call ''Cuckoo'' and I'll see if I can point to you without looking first...Now you try'. She will probably find it more difficult, even at three, than you imagine. Make it fun for her – 'Don't just guess, you have to listen carefully'.

Change the level of the sound by bending down low and calling, then standing on a chair – 'Can you find me down here and up here?' or 'Can you hear me behind the arm chair?' Make a growly voice for teddy, and a squeaky voice for dolly, and ask 'Who is talking now?'

Practise pitching your voice, and say: 'When you come close, whisper – don't shout in my ear, it gives me a fright!' When she is further away she can speak more loudly, but when she is close 'I can hear more easily'. Then, 'If I cover my ears I can't hear – so louder please. Can you make me hear properly when you ''talk'' to the wall, or hide behind a cushion or a chair? Pop up and say ''Pow!'''. It is rather like an adult voice training game, where you focus and direct your voice towards an outstretched hand.

THE NEED FOR RITUAL AND CEREMONY

There are many learned books written about why, as human beings, we need and enjoy a certain amount of ritual and ceremony in our lives. It is thought to be a means of regulating and formalizing our relationships within a group, smoothing our 'rites of passage' and taking the heat out of conflict. Some anthropologists trace it back to primitive 'sympathetic' magic and ceremonies aimed at making the crops grow. Bonding together in some sort of group occasion to celebrate or prepare for battle would have required an order of procedure.

I think that perhaps the need for ritual or an established way of proceeding provides safe, recognizable patterns within which we can function, without having to make constant and cumbersome decisions. It has been laid down for us, tried, tested and ready. At its most elementary, you can see the way children the world over play the same group games which are highly ritualistic. Versions of hop-scotch, five stones, hide-and-seek, ring games, and many others, are universal.

Children today often lack in many ways this safe framework of ceremony. Etiquette has tended to be debunked as being socially divisive, good manners are more a matter of lifestyle than elaborate ceremony, and games are far less prevalent in streets which are no longer safe for children. Even the much-loved routine of bedtime, waking, regular walks and set meal times, are almost non-existent for some children.

It is difficult for them to learn to behave within any sort of structure when it has little or no part in their lives. They are missing out on a deep human need, and only through ritual play can the balance be redressed.

The Tea Ceremony

Much is written about 'eating together', bonding with your children round the dining table, everyone sitting up straight and making witty conversation. It

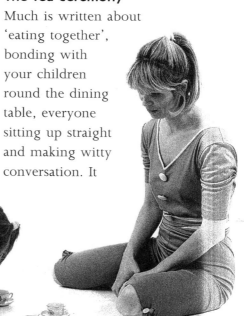

never seemed quite like that. 'Hurry up, it's getting cold – Don't talk with your mouth full – That's enough ketchup – Stop annoying one another!', is more like it. But you can satisfy the need for 'ritual' courtesy and conversation by having glorious fantasy meals together. Tea parties of exquisite politeness, perfect social interaction without the problems of washing up and mopping up.

Tiny cups and saucers require great dexterity and are a suitable size for small hands. Setting up a tidy table, counting cups and saucers, matching shapes and colour, judging space and careful handling, all have educational implications. It provides a time when the child is in control, practising the social skill of sharing and giving and saying the right things in the right way.

Pobs pours the tea with the utmost care, asking if Lala likes milk and sugar. She offers a biscuit, handing the plate with a concerned 'Would you like to choose?' It has all the stylized ritual of a Japanese tea ceremony, but is a small enchanted world, absolutely real to the child. 'Thank you so much for my delicious tea' is received with smiles of rapturous satisfaction. This sort of fantasy ritual is a very important part of childhood development. You can play it in the bath with 'real water'

when they are younger. It can develop into more elaborate creative games as they grow up. The tea ceremony can become a shopping and cooking venture for example.

There is time for real conversation. Listen carefully and you will learn a great deal of how she perceives the world. Don't be too depressed when you hear your own voice in her endless instructions – 'Don't scuff your shoes... Now look what you've done... I told you not to'. Children are being constantly corrected, doubtless with necessity, but fantasy play is a great safety valve. It is a time for being 'let off the hook' and reversing roles for a change. You will discover sides of each other's personalities not always seen: a chance to be charming, a chance for your child to be in control and to supervise you.

Dressing Up

Pobs and Lala are here 'Choosing hats for a wedding'. Dressing up is simple enough, but it makes adult and child equal parties. They are having a real discussion about shape and colour, opinions as to 'suitability' and which

way round to wear them. Opinions were accepted or turned down with reason, some were dropped and choices made. Pobs took great care to see that Lala was happy. There was a lot of talk of 'whom' they might be and where hats were usually worn, would they be warm enough and whether it would rain. Would their hats be all right if they got wet, and how to cope if they weren't. Given time, this could develop into very creative play.

There was real dialogue, respect for each other's opinions, interaction as two friends making sensible deci-sions, and no-one being pushed or taking the lead. Equal partners having fun together — learning, in fact, how to be good friends.

Playing Houses

Building houses, or creating a space for themselves, is one of the most compulsive forms of childhood play. Ideally, there should be the means — rugs and blankets, cushions and chairs — which can be built into 'personal palaces'. It is difficult when things have to be tidied away or space is limited. As a great treat, occasionally they might be left overnight. It is interesting that they never seem 'right' the following day, and a passionate reconstruction usually ensues at once.

'Houses' are a great feat of engineering for a small child. The sheer mechanics of setting up the chairs, judging height and space, getting the roof to 'stick' are a lesson in applied mathematics. It also involves accepting help and advice and working as a team, which are uneasy disciplines for under-fives and very good practice in social skills.

Whether it is a nest, fortress, or a work of art, any interference is vehemently resisted. Pobs was outraged when we tried to change a chair to make a tidier picture. She insisted, 'No, no — that's the right chair'.

'Houses' provide endless opportunities for the best sort of creative play. They can 'fill out' anything missing in the child's own life, such as the lack of their own bedroom. Only in fantasy can the

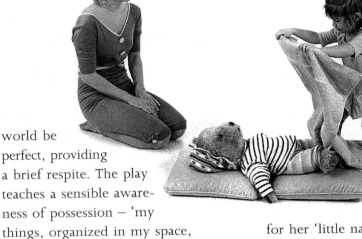

world be perfect, providing a brief respite. The play teaches a sensible aware-ness of possession – 'my things, organized in my space, organized by myself'.

It is an excellent preparation for making decisions and organizing their space, being in charge, and identifying with more adult responsi-bilities. An invitation to enter, however uncomfortable the 'house' may be, must be accepted with delight. It is no mean honour.

Tender Loving Care

It is touching to watch a child taking care of an adored teddy or doll, or indeed a younger one or little friend. This is another time to watch and listen carefully and never to interrupt unless they get into a muddle. They need to feel totally responsible and in charge.

Mrs Honey is Lala's teddy, but has been loved by all the children. Pobs made her a bed with the cushions and towel for her 'little nap'. She handled her very gently, tucking her up and speaking softly. Using 'soft' hands requires great skill and comes with practice and maturity. However good the intentions, they seldom achieve this before three. Try not to be overly cross when under-fives squeeze too hard, shatter anything delicate, push when they are supposed to pat gently, and fail to grasp the concept of light touch. They simply cannot quite manage it yet.

Learning to be kind and to care about others is an essential element in human relationships. Loving and giving is a deep and fundamental human need, without which life has little joy. Matching it up with the right expression in movement takes time and practice. This can make being kind to the new baby or the family pet a bit hazardous.

Lala was given twin dollies when her twin brothers were born. She used to tell me very firmly that I could look after 'the dolls' while she managed the 'baby boys'. She obviously felt it was I who needed the play therapy. This sort of ' parenting' play is also the natural way for children to reassure themselves. They can express their anxieties and find sensible solutions. Pobs told Mrs Honey in soothing tones 'I'll leave the light on and I'll come back if you hear the thunder'.

Without having too many deep psychological insights, children, given the opportunity, will 'play out' their problems in a creative and wholly satisfactory way. It is a vitally important method of coping with anxiety, and can sometimes seem quite repetitive and obsessional. That is part of the 'cure' and should not be deflected or interrupted.

Getting ready for a new school and visits to hospital can involve repeated playing of the scene with a doll or teddy. While reassuring the toy, they are reassuring themselves.

It is no exaggeration to say that many of our basic attitudes to parenting and caring for others are absorbed in our early years. While talking to my children, I could often 'hear' my mother's voice. Listening to Lala speak to Pobs, I often hear my own.

WHAT ABOUT DISCIPLINE?

The old adage that children need boundaries is as true today as it ever was. Uncomprehending disobedience puts any child at serious risk to life and limb. For this reason, as much as for your mutual sanity, recognized limits have to be set.

The problem is that there is now no common solid body of what could be called 'acceptable behaviour'. Lifestyles vary so much. Lying on a sofa munching a chicken bone and watching the television would be an outrage in one house-hold, but a daily lunchtime procedure next door. You need to decide where you stand. Once the limits are set you must stick to them.

Don't ever mind about being unpopular. It will pass anyway, and you have a perfect right to decide what you will tolerate. It is best to be realistic about your own standards. Two sets of rules simply won't work. 'Tidy your room at once' carries little conviction if the kitchen looks like a bombsite.

Whatever the rules might be, small children will look for the outer edges. After all, how do you know where to stop until you hit the barrier? They try every trick in the book and are uncanny experts at finding your every hang-up and exploiting every weakness. Their sense of timing is perfect.

You can usually spot the crisis coming and often head it off. It is rather like a takeover bid when the tension mounts and the demands become ever more outrageous. I remember my son, Julian, at about four, being increasingly obstreperous all through a wet Saturday. The crunch came in church on Sunday. He dashed ahead and walked backwards down the aisle in front of the vicar, singing 'Squashed tomatoes to you...' very loudly, to the tune of 'Happy Birthday'. Safely out of reach, as I was caught behind in the crowd making furious grabbing gestures in the air, his triumph was complete. Even after a 'letter' of apology, he still insisted that 'we thought it was funny and we laughed' – I never did discover whose idea it was.

It is a good trick to separate outrageous behaviour (in whatever forms) from the children themselves. Discuss it as an event which some-how 'happened' and which needs to be sorted out like a housekeeping problem. No child likes to feel foolish, and the suggestion that some

behaviour makes people 'ridiculous' ('How would you like it if I did a handstand in your school hall?' I once suggested) brings real alarm. This is far more effective than threats of reprisals.

The average child does not need 'psycho-babble' and endless, earnest explanations. Besides, they need to be 'in opposition' sometimes, cooking up their own schemes, and not always being identified with your ideas. 'Good behaviour' in an adult sense is something of a bonus. Quite apart from 'manners', there is a great deal for them to learn about their own reactions. From the serene to the volatile, temperaments vary vastly. They need to be left intact as part of life's basic equipment.

They need practical guidelines on suitable behaviour and how to cope with themselves. Perhaps it is more a matter of what you are than what you do. In the end every child must learn to manage her or himself.

What is naughtiness? There is only one sort of absolutely unacceptable behaviour, and that is being unkind. Noise, squabbling, broken mugs or holes in the flower beds, all must be forgiven. Children, like everyone else, are not budding angels, but the deliberate intention to hurt or distress another child, animal or any other person, needs firm and uncompromising disapproval. What's to be done?

Whatever it is, it needs to be done at once. Under-twos need swift removal. After that, try to avoid saying 'go to your room' – bedrooms should be havens, not prison cells. Standing outside the door to cool off will do just as well. Move in quickly, kneel on the floor in front of her, holding her arms very tightly against her sides. Keep a firm grip and wait for her to steady up. Insist on eye contact. Don't start lecturing and 'being reasonable' – she won't even listen, let alone understand. Say clearly: 'That was unkind and disgraceful – you will say you're sorry at once'. We used to say 'I beg your pardon', as it takes a good deal longer to say than 'Sorry'. Don't forget that you too will sometimes be the one to apologize, and be just as embarrassed and anxious to put it all behind you.

How bad is smacking? Children cannot cope with extremes of any sort. They do not have the reserves of strength and experience to manage big emotional dramas and set-piece punishments. Mistakes happen, sometimes intentional, sometimes

not. With fair warning and a clear understanding of your particular set limits, every child will grasp instinctively the need for justice.

The odd quick smack on the bottom, raised voice, or even demented exasperation are registered and quickly forgiven. Life is for getting on with. You can't spend the whole day in 'sweet reasoning' or high emotion over some early morning argument. There will be plenty more encounters, so try to keep a sense of perspective and focus on the things that interest and please.

ChildsPlay, with its emphasis on mutual good manners and on respect for each other's space, helps to establish a feeling of care which can underpin and colour the rest of your relationship.

Many parents and minders confirm our belief that sibling quarrels and rivalry are helped immeasurably through playing together. Far more effective than constant 'sorting out' which has no end, get on with the next game, dance a bit and concentrate on moving about which, in the end, is what children love most.

18 A SPECIAL KIND OF LOVING

Like everything else about children, they are happiest in the 'temperate zone'. Within certain limits and inconsistencies in a relationship, they bounce back unscathed. They need a warm, secure, workable, day-to-day relationship that allows them time for themselves. There should always be a safety net of unquestioning acceptance, that 'cocoon of kindness', which is never affected by anything they might do. Without it, children are terrifyingly vulnerable.

Extremes of adulation, deep or constant disapproval, favouritism (real or imagined), swings of mood, or the high drama of some adult relationships, are anathema to children, and potentially devastating. They do not have the terms of reference and can be made anxious and even damaged for life. You don't have to tell them everything – they cannot always understand.

As adults, it is sometimes difficult to be consistent or in total sympathy

with every changing phase of childhood (loving them is not a uniform commodity) – How did that tiny white bundle become that tantrum-throwing two-year-old? Children can be equally baffled by themselves, and often enjoy 'regressing' and becoming more baby-like than their age suggests. They are not always ready to move on to the next stage.

I never think there should be too much questioning and soul searching: most of us try hard enough, and they need our warmth and approval more than our constant scrutiny. Children love, and need to love, themselves best. 'I'm so clever...I'm so pretty...I'm so strong...I can do everything I like' are quite routine comments from a happy child. All children need that vital spark, that inextinguishable belief in themselves, to be left undimmed. Love and generosity to others can only begin here. All through life, and when the going gets tough, we need an unshakeable faith in ourselves.

'My space and your space.' Children need to feel happy and at ease in their 'own space'. Find time to talk, sometimes without actually touching. Listen carefully and enjoy

the different view of one another – as linked but separate people. This is called 'respecting each other's space' and liking one another's social skills. It is very 'grown up' and companionable, like two old friends.

'Our space.' Cuddles are about comfort and closeness, loving and giving. It is 'your space' together, and part of the essential bonding between you and your child. Being nursed and feeling close is a fundamental need of all young creatures. They require it for their emotional and mental development and, indeed, for their very survival. Some children appear to be more

sensual and more in need of physical contact than others. This can never in any way involve adult sexuality. Children need to be loved on their own terms and in complete trust.

Whether the cuddles are a laughing game, for healing a bumped knee, or for being close and relaxing together, your child will decide. You cannot insist on affection, and even a hug held for a second too long will provoke a furious 'Let me go! – Put me down!'. 'Enough' is what to aim for, and your child will let you know.

It always seems a little sad when people say of their children 'I adore them really, but...', instead of 'I really adore them'. Most of us know that loving our children is a commitment and investment for life. For us, it may simply light up the day and make life a little sweeter. But for any child, a stable, loving relationship is the difference between light and darkness, joy and confusion. It is all that makes sense of a baffling universe and enables her or him to say to *others* with ease and happiness: 'I love you too!'

19 MOVE AS YOU LEARN

Basic learning is, for all young creatures, about acquiring survival skills and moving happily on to the next phase of development. They need peak fitness to meet all the new challenges of fast developing bodies. (See page 35.) They need to grasp a complex set of social skills. (See page 89.) They need also a working basis on which to build educational concepts and acquire the basic tools of learning.

Eyes and ears take over eventually as the main means of learning. For under-fives, however, with their innate difficulty in sitting still long enough to sneeze let alone pore over a book (see page 34), they are happiest being able to learn directly through moving their whole bodies.

Like the little kittens (page 70), it is their natural way. It spreads the net of absorbing what we call 'the learning factors'. They practise a variety of skills while performing some quite simple task, e.g. in selecting and moving a red skittle from the basket, they are not only making a decision about number and colour; they are also judging distance, using a suitable movement 'effort' (see page 00), matching movement with verbal instructions, improving hand-eye co-ordination, experiencing cause and effect, learning to concentrate and remember, to set and finish a task, undoubtedly to add a few improvised touches of their own, and much more besides!

They will associate learning with fun, not something separate to be tackled whilst tied to a desk. It is a non-stop adventure for every waking moment.

Why the Skittles?

We used the skittles because they were new to Pobs. They are brightly coloured, attractively packaged, and she was intrigued. Their shape matches up with the original Medau clubs. They have also enormous potential for improvised learning and fantasy play.

Children must learn how to approach a new task and to move in a sensible progression. When introducing something new to a child, always give her time to 'explore' carefully and try out some ideas of her own. One thing at a time is the rule, which is why opening too many Christmas presents often ends in tears.

Like the 'conversations with an armchair', your child will react very differently at different ages. Pobs, with all the concern of a three-year old, disliked any idea of a game which knocked the skittles over. At two, knocking them about would doubtless have been the major interest. At five, the focus would have been on learning the technique of bowling the ball and winning the game.

If I describe their conversation as Lala and Pobs

unpacked and investigated the skittles, drawing out some of the learning factors, you will see just what potential for learning a simple task can provide:

'Let's unpack them carefully in case they break easily. **(Sensible approach to a new task)**

They're called skittles – no, we don't have to knock them over if you don't want to. **(Response to Pobs' own idea)**

They do look like bottles – this is the fat part and this is the neck. **(Shape)**

Let's pop the cork and pour out a drink. **(Fantasy/amusement memory)**

Which end will stand up – they're hard to balance on the floor. **(Hand-eye co-ordination)**

Can you balance it on your head – can you walk about? **(Balance)**

Can you feel how cool and smooth they are? **(Texture/temperature)** They all feel the same – exactly the same – except what? Yes – the colours, and you see those, not feel them.'
(Distinguishing the senses)

They used them as rolling pins and discovered the shape made when twisted around. **(Cause and effect)**

They rubbed their hands together around the neck, and made them spin as they let go. **(Firm touch)**

Skittles bounce a bit when they fall – 'but not like a bouncy ball'.

'Catch it this way, then sideways on. **(Effort and judgement)**

Shake it, wriggle it like a fish on the ground. Let's run about making our fish swim into the basket. **(Using the space)**

It's a lobster-pot – remember that last summer?' **(Recall)**

There was a hectic game 'swimming' the skittles into the basket. **(Stamina/letting off steam)**

Naming the colours and counting out loud as they 'swam' in gave a real sense of purpose. They shook the basket to make the fish 'jump' **(Using large muscle groups)**:

'They can't get out unless we tip them up. **(Cause and effect)**

Let's rescue them. **(Skill)**

Whoosh – here they come.

Listen to the sound: they're quite light, so they don't make a loud noise. It sounds like the rain on the roof. **(Sounds/listening)**

This way round they look like space rockets, not fish. Countdown – 10, 9, 8, 7, 6, 5, 4, 3, 2, 1, 0 – Lift-Off! **(Counting backwards)**

It's harder to lift them up, isn't it? Much easier to drop them down.'

By this time, Pobs was completely familiar with the skittles. She understood about their colour, weight and texture, how they 'reacted' to throwing and catching, and the possibility of energetic fun games. In fact, she was 'hooked', and ready for more concentrated learning themes.

This creative approach is crucial to children. Insensitively handled, it could all have ended in an argument about playing a 'proper' game of skittles. This is a disaster. It is a complete negation of the way small children learn, and serves only to crush their initiative and instinctive curiosity.

It is an immeasurable help to children who are slow starters or who have 'special needs' to learn at their own pace, without ever encountering any insuperable difficulties and sense of failure. Our Childsplay children are never bored. They see and understand the potential for creative play everywhere, making decisions and tackling new projects with delight and greater confidence.

COLOUR CODING

'Shall we sort out the skittles in colours? **(Selection and judgement)** Tell me the names – red, blue, yellow. They're all mixed up. Shall we put them in colour groups? All the blues together here, red there...that's right, they're identical now. **(Matching)**

Shall we put them up in lines?' **(Hand-eye co-ordination)**

These patterns were repeated, and different combinations made – 2 blue, 1 red, 3 yellow, etc. Lala and Pobs discussed which colour was the favourite, which matched and which were contrasts. **(Making choices)**

Which colours were the darkest, lightest and brightest? **(Observation)**

They arranged them in order, starting with white as the lightest. **(Judging shades)**

'Blue and green are nearly the same. Can you see anything else that's blue? Yes, your shoes. That one's green – grass is green too, and that bright yellow is just like a dandelion.' **(Matching colour)**

SHAPES AND SPACE

Some children are very word worthy, while others are more excited by shapes and space. Perhaps it is what makes poets different from architects? You don't have to work at it – one shape at a time is enough.

'Let's put the skittles in a straight line – from here to here – in this direction.' **(Direction)**

Now make two parallel lines with a path between to walk through. 'Let's change them and make a wall – put the skittles close together, no spaces, and see if we can hide behind it. It's not very high – so we can't hide unless we lie down. **(Comparative sizes)**

Let's peep over and say "Whoosh" to the pigeons. **(Change of pace)**

Let's walk along with one foot on either side like a bridge. Let's creep round – don't knock them down. **(Muscular control)**

Now we're looking the other way.' **(Image and direction)**

You can change the shape of the line by moving the skittles to form a curvy line, criss-cross, two semi-circles, horseshoes and arrow-shape. 'Walk' the line along by moving a skittle from the end of the line and adding it on to the other end.

Make a shape – 'We can curve them round into a circle. Put one in the centre: it looks like a wheel'. Make big and little squares. **(Dexterity/size)**

You will find many combinations – it requires great dexterity to put a square around a circle, for example. You can also make numbers and letters – 1, 2, 3, A, B, C – and change

colours. Let her stand on a chair to see the figures.

'Let's push them over and muddle them up – they won't break, even if we throw them around. **(Unstructured play)**

They have been a nuisance, falling over like that.' **('Appropriate' aggression)**

You can make pretty, 'flat' patterns if you put the skittles on their sides.

'Let's pick out the yellow ones and put them in a circle with their necks facing each other. Look – it's a daisy!' **(Abstract creation)**

Make a poinsettia with red skittles, with the fat ends together in the middle.

Over-fours love making complicated patterns. You can use the hoops for frames, and colour-match or contrast the skittles in the middle. It is the same idea as any coloured shapes game, but involves more physical dexterity and a larger scale. You can do similar things with bean bags, coits, children's building-bricks, coloured paper or plastic shapes.

NUMBERS AND COUNTING

Children gain great pleasure in counting skittles – it gives them a firm grasp of numbers and takes them into simple sums. Skittles are ideal counters, and here are some ideas to start you off:

Count how many skittles there are altogether, and how many different colour groups. See how many there are in each group.

'Find me 2 red and 3 green, etc... Look, you can hold the necks of the skittles in your fingers, like a milkman.

How many pints would you like, Mrs Honey?' You can deliver milk to the toys.

Think up silly places to put the skittles – one in each hand, one under the chin, and one tucked under the elbow – and count them. Make it jokey.

'How many do you have? How many can I hold in my lap? My arms? My knees? How many can you wrap up in the towel? How many can we stand on the seat of the arm chair, or in the middle of the hoop?'

Lala and Pobs are playing simple 'sums'. The variations are endless, and can develop naturally into more complicated number games of adding, subtracting, division and multiplying. Do 4 claps for 4 skittles: 1, 2, 3, 4. Add one more skittle, makes – 1, 2, 3, 4 and 5. Take 2 away, makes: 1, 2, 3. Take 1 away, makes: 1, 2.

Set them up any way you both like. Put them into groups: for example, 4 skittles here, and 2 here. 'Which are mine?'

Put 6 here and 3 here. 'Which group is smaller?'

Older children like to space out the skittles in 'bundles' such as 2+2+2 and 2+4 or 5+1.

You can make simple number cards together. 'Find me the "2" card and put it with 2 skittles. 2 and 2 makes 4.'

You can play out of doors with other children. When moving about, learning 'numbers' becomes enormous fun.

I REMEMBER WHERE...

Simple memory training games are a favourite. Play as partners to begin with as some children always prefer a combined effort.

'Let's hide a skittle. Where shall we put it – under the cushion? We'll walk about and talk to Mrs Honey, then see if we can still remember **(Place memory)**

One is easy. Now let's hide 1, 2, 3, 4, more. (**Increasing concentration**)

Can you remember where we put the red one, and the green one?

Did we put 2 in the same place?

Which one did we hide first?

Which was standing and which one was lying down?' (**Listening to verbal instructions**)

You can leave the clubs hidden and point to the places, retrieve them and start afresh, or find them all at the end, depending on the age and skill of the child or small group. They will soon remember far better than you do and will usually tell you so.

'You don't remember anything, do you?'

'You'll have to be patient with me!'

Pobs and Lala are remembering which colour club was in which hand. Where is the blue one? Curiously, children seldom get it right at first, even in their own hands. You can vary the idea by putting one behind, one up your jumper, one under your knees. Which colour went where? They do have to concentrate and learn about right and left.

'TOP OF THE POPS'

Pobs decided to use the skittle as a microphone and sing, shaking her head like a pop star. There are scores of marvellous nursery rhymes and songs for children. Sing to your

baby from day one, in the bath, in the park, in the car. Sing every song you ever knew. Some children have an excellent idea of pitch, and can hold a tune. Others, like Pobs, are better at recitative and made-up story songs which go on and on. 'This is long way, OK?', she often says.

Singing is the key to fluent speech. There are dozens of tapes and records made especially for children that allow you to sing and play along. They will listen to anything if it has a good strong beat. You can play along with the music (Pobs pretended the skittle was a maracca and then beat the floor as a drum accompaniment). Toy xylophones, drums and penny-whistles, kitchen spoons, or even dried peas in a carton, make excellent instruments.

There is so much 'multiple' sound about today that it is good to encourage children to listen for specific sounds, isolating them from the background 'clutter'. Walk about, holding the bowl of a wooden spoon, tapping anything and everything with the handle. 'Listen to the tap-tap-tap on the chair – it's different from the floor.' Talk about sound: 'Now, don't look, and see if you can remember which sound this was...' Make them fairly obvious at first.

Listen to sounds everywhere –

blackbirds singing, the stone thrown into the water, wind in the trees, feet on the mat, dry leaves, bouncing tennis balls, cars, planes and lawnmowers. The experience of music and an easy grasp of sound, pitch and rhythm, long before any formal music training has begun, is an additional joy in childhood.

REVERSING ROLES

Children are so constantly organized and receiving instructions, that it is beneficial to reverse roles frequently. Try to find a time each day when you reverse roles, even if it is only saying : 'What a good idea', 'Show me the way to the shops', or 'Teach me how to hop'.

Initiating ideas and not simply following, is a vital part of a child's education. They are so naturally brilliant at it. Carrying it out is another matter. But they do become very discouraged and frustrated if never allowed to try.

Pobs and Lala are taking time to beat a rhythm on the floor with the skittles. 'You play for me to dance, and then I'll play for you'. You can start with ordinary marching steps which go faster and slower. Progress to all sorts of ideas and variations. Use heavy beats for 'giant's feet' and light taps for 'butterflies'. Beat 'tippy-toes' with the thin end and 'flat feet'

be very flexible and creative, swapping ideas and thinking 'on her feet'. You will both learn to treat each other with respect and patience. It is essential too that children learn to carry out instructions and remember a sequence of movements. It is an important 'safety factor' in children's lives and, taught through play, becomes instinctive.

We call the game 'Tell me what to do'. It begins with a rhyme said with hand-clapping, as a question-and-answer session. Sit facing each other and say:

'Please tell me, tell me what to do.'

'Listen hard, and I'll tell you...'

It's a good game for a group of children, too. Set an easy task which the child has to perform tidily and quickly without falling over, forgetting or kicking the furniture.

with the fat end; 'ski steps' with the skittle flat and pushed forwards. Here, Pobs is lifting the club up high to indicate slow, high knee-stepping.

Lala is bouncing the skittles in a galloping rhythm – 'a-gallop-a-gallop-a-gallop' – for Pobs to do pony skips. Five-year-olds can do complicated patterns, combining steps and skips, running and stepping, galloping sideways, and playing the appropriate rhythm. Two-year-olds will enjoy the idea of the game, but the beating and bouncing around will probably not match up.

This sort of game will teach her to

Lala has asked Pobs to run around her twice and then sit down on her cushion facing the other way. Any other ideas will do:

'Run to the chair – sit down – get up – come back. Hop across the room, skip back – roll over twice on the floor – then stand by the chair.'

By three, they can usually remember and execute three separate moves. By five, they appreciate complicated tasks, such as:

'Take three steps forward – skip to the door – head over heels into the middle of the room – turn round twice, and walk back to me like a camel.'

You can play it in the park with other children, turning it into a dropping-out game when they make a mistake or forget. They like to speed it up:

'Count and see how fast I am!' Insist that they must be tidy and not a shambles.

Children love jokes. Put a slipper

on your head, carry a towel in your teeth, balance the skittle on your nose – it will provoke shrieks of laughter. This sort of game, played with amusement and tact, is an invaluable learning tool. Concentration, remembering a sequence, matching words with actions, performing with aplomb, and all the fitness elements combine. The trouble is that, like the memory game, they will soon be much better at it than you. I've heard too often, 'You don't remember, do you – you don't remember what you told me to do.' Perhaps it's good for adult concentration as well!

BUSY FINGERS, MAGIC HANDS

According to anthropologists, the way we use our hands is one of the basic classifications that make us human beings. That first dab at a fuzzy duck suspended over our pram is the beginning of a lifetime's fascination with all that 'manual dexterity' can achieve. Every great project of human endeavour depends in its design stage on the clever use of someone's hands. From surgery to sewing, from music-making to games playing, from cooking to loving and caring, the first contact is through our hands.

With all this restless energy and incredible potential, it is easy to see why small children never stop practising. Those little fidgeting fingers are never still. I remember my brother dismantling my dollies' sewing-machine whilst assuring me that he could 'mend it'. We never managed to make it work, but we spent hours involved with twiddling bolts and fitting screws and levers.

The connections in the brain between hand, eye and mouth are very close (see page 90). In stimulating one sense, we are awakening others. Hands, in any case, have a special energy of their own. We instinctively grip our hands or press them together to gather our courage. We cover our faces in sadness and clap our hands in delight.

DEVELOPING A SENSE OF TOUCH

Small children are intrigued by textures. They can be totally absorbed in stroking the carpet or tearing paper. Babies look first, touch with their hands, try to taste, and look again, repeating the sequence over and over again. (See photograph, page 27.)

Stimulate this natural curiosity by providing lots of variety of textures – an orange, a wooden spoon, a woolly ball and a sponge will do. Try to find 'living' substances (wooden bricks, a cotton handkerchief, shells or a flat stone). Plastic toys have no surface interest, are always the same temperature, and are often brightly coloured or make noises, which stimulate senses other than touch.

FROM 8 MONTHS

Sit her on your lap facing you. Hold her hands and touch your hair with them:

My hair is soft -
My cheek is smooth,
My teeth are hard...
Yum, yum, eat you up!

This is a good chorus which you can throw in at any time, pretending to munch her fingers, neck or tummy:

My knees are hard,
My legs are plump,
My ears feel odd...
Yum, yum, eat you up!

As they grow older, point out all sorts of different 'feels'. 'Feel Mrs Honey – she's so soft. Her eyes are hard and smooth and her nose is hard and crinkly. You've got hard buttons on your soft jumper..
The carpet is smooth, the doormat is prickly. The floor is hard, the cushion is soft'.

They all love to feel water running over fingers and toes, warm or cold. Mud, sand, earth, bark, wet leaves, sticky fingers (my pet aversion), all provide delicious sensations.

Some years ago, I taught a group of blind children who had wonderfully sensitive fingers. They had a series of little cotton bags which contained various objects – a pencil, carrot, marbles and spoon among them. They could tell in a flash what was inside by feeling the bag.

THE FEELIE GAME – 'THINK' WITH YOUR FINGERS

You can use this idea with a sock into which you put things for her to feel and recognize: a comb, ping-pong ball, eraser, wooden bead, hair grip or farm animal. You can play it any way you like, with several objects to a sock or one in each of several socks. She will find it difficult and will need to concentrate hard at first. You must 'play' too – 'I wonder what this could be?'

'GUESS WHO?'

Put some soft toys into a pillow case. Both put your arms in and guess who you can feel. 'Is this Piggy? No, it's Grey Rabbit because I can feel his ears.'

Make it fun pulling out each toy to check. 'The toys like the bag and are jumping back in...or is the rabbit hopping away?'

Discuss what made each one

distinguishable – Elephant has a trunk, Foxy has a long tail, Teddy has round ears. Children under four usually need to use both hands, which is curious. Employing one hand is completely baffling, and they will say 'I can't feel anything'.

'WAKE UP HANDS'

From the baby clapping games 'Pat-a-cake' and others (see page 91), you can play some simple rhythm games together. Pobs and Lala are playing a very basic game, clapping each other's hands – both hands together to start with, and in a slow careful rhythm. Clap on each word. It is easier for you to be sitting.

Clap hands, clap hands, (4 claps on hands)
Clap hands together, (clap each other's hands)
Clap up, (2 claps above heads)
Clap down, (2 claps at tummy level)
And clap the ground. (4 claps on the ground)

By four, they enjoy faster, more complicated rhymes which require high levels of co-ordination and concentration.

One example includes:

A sailor went to sea, sea, sea,
To see what he could see, see, see,
But all that he could see, see, see,
Was the bottom of the deep blue sea, sea, sea.

You can clap this any way you like, but the traditional way is to clap your own hands together, clap right hands across, clap together, then left hands across. On each see, see, see, clap opposite left and right hands together.

By five, they will be moving very fast and you will be the one making the muddles!

'Flat Hands' is another favourite. Put your hands down flat, alternating with hers, one on top of the other. Pull out the bottom hand and place it on the top. It requires a great deal of concentration for a small child. Move rhythmically with the rhyme:

> One hand on top,
> First yours, now mine,
> One under, one up,
> We change all the time.

Make it faster when she has grasped the pattern.

BUSY FINGERS

Look at your hands together and discuss the size and shape, palms up or palms down. Draw around them with a felt tip pen – 'This is an outline of the shape'. Talk about fingers and thumbs, draw in the nails or palm lines on the paper and colour in the shapes or cut them out. Encourage suggestions – 'Shall we make another set and colour them in like woolly gloves? And see if they match our hands?'

Hold up her hands and name each finger. Start with the thumb and the little finger (we call them Thumbkin and Pinkie). 'See if they can meet and dance together – two fat Thumbkins dance together, now my two little Pinkie fingers can dance together.'

By three, you can add the other fingers, e.g. Pointer, Longman and Ringman, and practise moving them separately. You can chant as you wriggle them about:

> Dance Thumbkin, dance
> Dance Pointer, dance
> Dance Longman, dance
> Dance Ringman, dance
> Dance Pinkie, dance
> We'll all dance together
> Whenever we get the chance.

(Shake your hands and twiddle all your fingers together).

There are excellent books on hand and finger games, which children thoroughly enjoy. You can combine them with bursts of dashing about if she starts to get restless.

> Here is a bird, (Link thumbs and flap hands)
> Here is a tree, (Make hands into fists on top of each other)
> Here is a nest, (Cup your hands)
> With eggs 1, 2, 3, (Hold up 3 fingers)
> Here is a pussy cat, (Make hands into paws and creep forward)
> Oh dear me!
> Fly away bird, (Run about flapping arms)
> To the top of the tree. ('Perch' up high on a chair)

The less energetic version of the last

two lines is to link thumbs again and 'perch' her hands on her head.

Children love their hands. Lala used to talk about 'my dear little hands'. Getting to understand them and enjoy the miracles they perform is a source of confidence and self-esteem. It involves loving and caring, and it establishes a sound working basis on which to build all the complicated skills which require 'manual dexterity'.

CHILDSPLAY WITH MORE THAN ONE

Lala and I teach and have taught children of all ages. ChildsPlay was originally conceived as a group activity, as something 'right' for the under fives.

It was the persistent requests of parents and minders of these under fives for a 'way to do class at home' that prompted the writing of this book. It is, therefore, easy to see that in skilled hands all the ideas adapt easily and apply directly to small or large groups of children. You will find that the main problem is finding a safe space and having enough equipment to go round. Remember too that any child under five climbing or 'changing levels' needs direct adult supervision.

ChildsPlay works well with a mixed age group, provided you all 'respect each other's space'. My children, the original 'gang of three', were the first guinea pigs and had enormous fun and undoubted benefits.

It is a good idea, however, to start with a one-to-one class as that 'special atmosphere' (see page 40) needs to be established first.

20 CHILDREN WITH SPECIAL NEEDS

We have an eyesight problem in the family, and I understand very well how easy it is to be anxious and overprotective. One can become very sensitive about receiving too much 'advice', and I offer these ideas with the greatest respect.

It does help to remember that all children tug your heartstrings on occasions. Whether it's a high fever, a painful illness, tears over a beloved pet, or 'what my best friend said to me', it is not easy to watch them cry.

You have to hang in there together and somehow grow through their distress. It is an inevitable part of being human.

Fortunately for the under-fives, their whole world is very small and self-centred. It is part of their survival kit. They cannot afford long-term depression, prolonged anxiety or self-pity. With a calm and sensible adult, as many cuddles as they ask for, and as much of a familiar routine as possible, they will instinctively focus on anything close at hand which pleases and diverts them.

It does not help if you are too frequently overwhelmed. There will always be times when you are battling with tears while they play and chatter on. Perhaps these are the small deceptions that your relationship will allow.

ChildsPlay, with its totally flexible approach, easily accommodates the 'special needs' of any child. It does help to clear your mind if you write down two lists with supposed difficulties on one side and positive advantages on the other.

I did this after teaching a group of blind and partially-sighted children for the first time. I was surprised to find how many advantages there were. The first one had become obvious almost at once. They were holding hands in a circle and I dashed to start the music tape. If you take too long, sighted children won't wait, and an 'alternative' class starts up immediately. My heart almost stopped when I turned round to find they had not moved at all. It became a very special pleasure to work at their easier pace. There were no problems of group discipline, and their delighted acceptance of any new project, the gradual input of their own ideas, and their charming care of one another, made the experience unforgettable.

I think that, as with all children, it is more a matter of emphasis on special areas than a completely altered approach. You will probably know instinctively how best to manage for your child. As her confidence increases, in no time at all she will be pointing out anything you might have missed. These areas will have to be addressed.

A blind child has difficulty with 'horizontal space', but is perfectly safe and happy running about if she can hold on to something – holding hands, or onto the plastic hoop or the end of a towel provides the necessary security. A piece of thick rope stretched out across the room or garden is an enormous help. They can bob about, duck under, run up and down, or sideways gallop with fingertip contact. Use the 'vertical' space too, i.e. getting up and down, as this is easy for them.

It also helps children with problems of co-ordination to move in contact with someone or something. It is a safe way to begin, as they all need to experience the high energy of getting puffed and excited. It is beneficial for all their body systems (see page 35) and, as their muscle tone improves, they will gain more control. Using hand apparatus increases their awareness and contact with things around them.

A deaf child can often feel impatient and frustrated. You need extra time to explain. Make sure you have eye contact, lots of facial expression, and hand gestures. It helps if you demonstrate and make a great joke about your efforts to run and jump about.

Concentrate on working at strength (see page 52). This is a great release for pent-up frustration. It can, after all, be infuriating if you see what everyone else is doing, but just need more time to hear and understand what it's about. Concentrate on all the skills (see page 71) which will help their co-ordination.

Slow learners and children with so-called 'personality disorders' need a gentler pace. Every small development is a triumph. Always start with something they can already manage: repetition is the key word. Make everything very clear, introducing only one new idea at a time. Never compare them with anyone but themselves.

It isn't helpful to set elaborate long-term goals. Like all children, they are a law unto themselves. Your praise and genuine pleasure in what they do will be more useful than an achievement plan. There should never ever be any sense of failure.

You need to be careful of your 'safe space'. I noticed that the blind children were very sensitive to bumps and scratches and took far longer to regain their confidence.

It is remarkable that responding to rhythm is the one 'sense' that remains strong in all children at every level of ability. Use the ideas about rhythm and music. (See page 112.) It is the great healer and motivator, and the benefits for you and your child will be infinite.

One last thought or gentle warning.

Children can become a sort of obsession, and a child with special needs seems to increase this possibility. The complicated emotions which grip one can lead to a consuming commitment or the opposite – intense rejection. Keep some part of your life separate if you can. There will be others who need you too, and you do, above all, need space and time for yourself.

If no-one expects the impossible, there are very great returns. Surprise yourself with your list of 'plusses'. Some of the most loving, charming and courageous children I have ever known, would qualify as 'special needs'. Even coping with the 'little tykes' – my father's favourite term for us when we were being especially wild – can bring its own humour and reward.

EPILOGUE

~~~

We must be all that we can be

MARIA MONTESSORI

I am an unashamed romantic about children. I love their energy and exasperating optimism. I find them endearing and endlessly funny. In every corner of the world they are surely the earth's most beautiful people.

But the real reason for my unwavering passion is that I believe in the power of those vivid first five years to illuminate or sadden the rest of our lives. Time never returns. There is no chance of a replay. We need to make it right for them first time round.

It is not really very difficult. We know that they need time, space and someone kind. In the scheme of things, this is not a lot.

Besides, most of the 'work' they will do for themselves.

Try not to hurry the little ones. There is a long and complicated way ahead. All that we need to think about is the excitement of the next big step.

Lucy Jackson BA Hons (London), doyenne of Medau in Britain, has taught fitness, movement and dance classes for almost forty years. Her enthusiasm and expertise have made her the most famous exponent of the Medau Method. She has taken the work all over the world and is the author of countless articles on Medau and health-related topics. Married to gynaecologist Ian Jackson, she has a daughter, Lala Manners, and twin sons.

Lala Manners BA Hons Dip Ed (London), Lucy's daughter, was born to the Medau Method and shares her mother's passion for movement. She has studied all fields of movement, dance and exercise, and teaches extensively. Renowned for her work with babies and children, she is becoming increasingly well-known for her appearances on television and throughout the media.

INDEX

Medau

THE ART OF ENERGY

Lucy Jackson

Medau is an exciting form of exercise combining the rhythm of dance with graceful, natural, whole body movement. It mixes aerobics and stretch – without straining the body. Whether you are 10, 20 or over 40 the movement can be done at the pace which is right for you.

The art of energy is a unique programme of Medau movements combining:

- ♦ Stretch
- ♦ Strength
- ♦ Stamina
- ♦ Suppleness

It will leave you fitter, leaner, healthier and full of confidence; and above all, it is enjoyable to do. So come alive with Medau! Throw away your gruelling repetitive routines and learn to be in tune with your body – the natural way.

THE POLYGRAM VIDEO

The bestselling video *Medau: The art of energy* is produced by Polygram and presented by Lala Manners.
The video is available from all good video stores and is priced from £10.99

Feeling Good

Stress-free movement, exercise and fitness for life

Lucy Jackson and Lala Manners

————

This unique exercise cassette is designed as a fitness 'top-up' or starting point for beginners. It is safe, manageable, and particularly suitable for the blind and visually impaired.
Devised and presented by the famous mother-daughter team, it is based on the Medau Method, which works with the natural body structure. The movements are effective and easy to follow, with obvious benefits to health and safety.

ChildsPlay

Movement Games for Fun and Fitness

Lucy Jackson Jackson and Lala Manners

————

Developed from the Medau Method, this cassette can be used either separately or in conjunction with *ChildsPlay* by Lucy Jackson. Fitness, creative play and natural development are of vital importance during a child's first five years, and here we are shown how they can be achieved by having fun.

Cassettes available by mail order from:
Motivation Sound Ltd,
35a Broadhurst Gardens
London NW6 3QT
Tel: 071 328 8305

MEDAU: THE ART OF ENERGY	Lucy Jackson	0 7225 2572 9	£6.99	⌐
BOOK OF CHILD CARE	Dr Hugh Jolly	0 04 649035 3	£8.99	⌐
A MOTHER'S INSTINCT	Cassandra Eason	1 85538 124 9	£5.99	⌐
NEW ACTIVE BIRTH	Janet Balaskas	0 7225 2566 4	£9.99	⌐
SPECIAL CHILDREN, SPECIAL NEEDS	Mary McCormack	0 7225 2598 2	£7.99	⌐
WATERBIRTH	Janet Balaskas & Yehudi Gordon	0 7225 2788 8	£9.99	⌐
YOUR SECOND BABY	Pamela Hewitt & Wendy Rose-Neil	0 7225 2594 X	£5.99	⌐

All these books are available from your local bookseller or can be ordered direct from the publishers.
To order direct just tick the titles you want and fill in the form below

Name _____

Address _____

_____

Postcode _____

Send to Thorsons Mail Order, Dept 3, HarperCollins*Publishers*,
Westerhill Road, Bishopbriggs, Glasgow G64 2QT.
Please enclose a cheque or postal order or your authority to debit your Visa/Access account

Credit card no. _____

Expiry date _____

Signature _____

– to the value of the cover price plus
UK & BFPO Add £1.00 for the first book and 25p for each additional book ordered.
Overseas orders including Eire Please add £2.95 service charge.
Books will be sent by surface mail but quotes for airmail despatches will be given on request.

24 HOUR TELEPHONE ORDERING SERVICE FOR ACCESS/VISA
CARDHOLDERS – TEL 041 772 2281.